The Clear
Cookbook

About the Author

Dale Pinnock is a renowned nutritionist, medical herbalist, chef and health expert with a burning interest in the way that food can be a powerful medicine. His passion is explaining to people, in a practical, fun and exciting way, how to easily make sense of the barrage of information about how food affects their health. He is a regular on television, radio and in the press, spreading this message far and wide.

Dale qualified in both Nutrition and Herbal Medicine and trained at the University of Westminster. He runs private healthcare clinics in Cambridgeshire and Hertfordshire where he combines herbal medicine with nutritional healing to provide a full and far-reaching therapeutic programme.

The Clear Skin Cookbook

How the right food
can improve your skin

Dale Pinnock

RIGHT WAY

Constable & Robinson Ltd
55–56 Russell Square
London
WC1B 4HP
www.constablerobinson.com

First published in the UK by Right Way,
an imprint of Constable & Robinson, 2012

A copy of the British Library Cataloguing in Publication Data
is available from the British Library

ISBN: 978-0-7160-2296-1

1 3 5 7 9 10 8 6 4 2

Printed and bound in China

Picture credits
Under Creative Commons License (CC by 2.0): p.6 © Jsome1; p.16 © Nick Harris1; p.24 © C.K.H.; p.32
© oropeza; p.39 © Vik Nanda; p.41 © color line; p.46 © Svadilfari; p.50 anolobb; p.52 © Vvillamon; p.57
cursedthing; p.59 © Juan Antonio Capó; p.62 © cwbuecheler; p.64 © stormwarning; p.66 © Dennis Wong;
p.70 © FotoosVanRobin; p.72 © kozumel; p.74 © Muffet; p.76 © indi.ca; p.84 © Fovea Centralis; p86 ©
telemetry9; p.98 © Darwin Bell; p.101 © The Ewan; p.103 © tillwe; p.105: © Charleston's TheDigitel; p.107
© *clairity*; p.110 © woodleywonderworks; p.117 © audreyjm529; p.119 © heathervescent; p.123 © Stewart;
p.128 © Jude Doyland; p.135 © macinate; p.154 © BoJay; p.157 © how lucky we are; p.159 © threelayercake;
p.167 © bgottsab; p.168 © janineomg; p.171 © OakleyOriginals; p.172 © Martin Cathrae; p.176 © Olga
Oslina; p.180 © leoncillo sabino; p.182 © layirving.
www.shutterstock.com: p.94 © Fedor Korolevskiy; p.114 © Yaroslava; p.124 © Olga Miltsova; p.131 ©
verdeskerde; p.137 © vichie81; p.143 © Lusoimages; p.150 © Stephen Snyder; p.160 © Olaru Radian-
Alexandru; p.164 © agorulko.

Contents

Introduction

I don't think there is anything that more greatly reflects someone's state of health than a person's skin. Healthy people have a wonderfully smooth glowing skin with even tone, and free from blemishes. Also, it is true to say, there is nothing more distressing than angry skin conditions, especially on areas of the body that are on display to the rest of the world, like the face and hands. This is something that I know well from my own personal experience. Although, if I hadn't gone through that, I wouldn't be sitting here writing this today.

One thing that is alarming is how many people have started appearing at my clinics with very angry skin conditions, and aggressive flare-ups, that they had never experienced in the past. Or young children with eczema so bad that it goes way beyond the normal childhood eczema that we would expect to see. Talking to other healthcare professionals, I found that this experience is true right across the board. I have friends who are doctors, friends who are acupuncturists, friends who are homeopaths, etc. They have all reported a similar increase in the amount of clients they see with bad skin lesions.

So what is causing this? I really feel that there isn't one particular factor, but it is the sum of all the challenges that modern life places upon our bodies that causes physical stress to multiple systems: pollution in our immediate environment; stress in our work and home lives; myriads of additives in our nutrient-devoid foods. All of these things act as a cocktail that burdens every system in the body, and can affect immunity, trigger or worsen inflammatory issues, and have been linked with the onset and progression of many chronic diseases.

I'd love to tell you that there is some magical food or lifestyle that will eradicate all of these issues and make your skin immune to any kind of upset or make it ageless. But, alas, this isn't the case. However, what I can certainly tell you is that diet and lifestyle will have a massive impact upon the health and functioning of the skin, the rate at which it ages, and the severity and healing time of skin lesions. That's what this book is about. No matter what area of skin health you are concerned with, there is information here regarding the nutritional link. Whether you are trying to tackle acne, have stubborn eczema, or would rather do the best you can to keep your skin looking young and healthy for as long as you can, then you are in the right place.

My Story

When I was ten years old, my body started to change. I noticed a few little bumps on my chin but I wasn't overly concerned at first. The only thing that mattered to me in those days was being able to get down to the lake after school and at the weekends to do some fishing.

However, it was different a year later when I left junior school to go to secondary school (high school). It was here that the trouble began. By this stage I was spotty. There's no other word for it. From forehead to chin, I was covered in nasty little red spots, a few bigger bumps and blackheads too. It didn't take long for everyone else in the class to notice this and I became the target of the usual names, such as Pizza face and Zit face.

At that stage in life, these things can make us very self-conscious and I became quite withdrawn, although I'd never let it show. By the time I reached the final year of school, it was a permanent distraction. I'd make a conscious effort to cover my face with a scarf, as I didn't want anyone to see my skin in daylight. Whenever I went into a shop or a building of any type, I could never stand or sit under the strip lighting because it would really show up my acne, and I would literally close up and disappear inside myself.

I went to doctor after doctor, specialist after specialist, and tried every conceivable lotion and potion they had to offer: strange sticky roll-on lotions, antibiotics, retinol gels, the works. Nothing whatsoever helped. One day, at the age of about 15–16, a friend's mum lent me a book on nutrition and natural healthcare. I remember her telling me, "Unless you look after what's going on inside, nothing will change on the outside." Now, as a teenage boy, I wasn't immediately impressed with that advice. However, I was so desperate that I read the book from cover to cover in a weekend. It changed my life: I gave up smoking, gave up eating meat, gave up most dairy products, and built a diet based on fruit, vegetables and whole grains, supplementing it with zinc, omega 3 and the B vitamins.

Just a little note

You will notice that the key points are repeated over and over in this book. This is an entirely intentional thing. Quite simply, I want you to be able to know and understand, inside and out, the way in which certain foods, nutrients, etc, affect your skin. This will give you a valuable tool to use when making food choices throughout your life. Once you know the basic nutrients in common foods and how these affect your skin, you can easily make the right choices, and develop this as a lifestyle that soon becomes second nature to you. I want you to be able to repeat the principles in your sleep. Enjoy and have fun with this journey.

The changes were incredible. My skin certainly did clear. The red aggressive acne eventually disappeared, leaving not even the slightest mark. Beyond that, my body and mind were completely transformed and an entirely new person was born.

I have seen the powerful effect that food can have on our health, first hand. It is simple yet profound. It was this experience that led me here today and has given me 100 per cent faith that if you implement the changes I recommend in this book, you too will start to see dramatic changes in the way your skin looks, not to mention the way that you feel inside.

1

What the Skin Does and How it Works

If I were to ask you what the largest organ in the body is, I should imagine that many of you would say the brain, or the lungs, or the liver. Well, believe it or not, it's our skin. Many of us don't think of our skin as an organ, but it is the biggest organ of the human body, weighing an average 2.7 kilograms (nearly 6 lb).

Key Functions of the Skin

The first major function of the skin is to act as a physical barrier to the outside world. All of our body's tissues are so delicate that just the most microscopic level of exposure to many external elements would be enough to kill us. The skin offers us protection.

An Extension of the Immune System

The skin is a fully fledged part of our body's immune system. This is partially due to the physical barrier it provides, but there is more to it than that.

The skin is covered in billions of bacteria. Several types of bacteria live happily and symbiotically on its surface. One of the roles that these tiny passengers can play is a defensive one against certain types of potentially pathogenic bacteria. This can be as a result of direct aggression towards the potential invader, or simply by competing for space on our skin's surface.

The skin can also help in the early stages of detection of a pathogen. There are cells embedded within the skin called Langerhans cells. These cells basically work as surveillance stations in the outer layers of the skin. They have the ability to detect specific pathogens and then communicate to our systemic immunity, via the lymphatic system, that trouble is coming.

Temperature Regulation

The skin is the key factor in regulating the temperature of the human body. The surface of the skin is highly sensitive (more on that later), and as such can detect the slightest change in environmental temperature. It relays this information back to our brain's main control centre, the hypothalamus, which has a defined set point of what the body temperature should be. If internal or environmental factors cause the actual temperature to deviate outside this set point, then the hypothalamus reacts to the signal by instigating the relevant responses to make the body warmer or cooler.

If we are too cold, the hypothalamus will send messages to the skin causing it to narrow the capillaries that supply it. This reduces heat loss through the surface of the skin. This is why we tend to look a little pale when we are cold. There is also a signal to the skeletal muscles that cause the body to shiver in order to generate heat.

When we are hot, nerve impulses sent to the skin cause the capillaries to dilate, allowing heat to escape through the skin's surface. The sweat glands are also stimulated and, as the sweat evaporates off the surface of the skin, it cools us down rapidly.

Sensory Organ

The skin is, of course, one of the major sensory organs, delivering the sense of touch. There are thousands of nerve endings within the skin, with some parts of the body (such as the fingertips) having higher concentrations than others. There are four main sensations that are transmitted through the skin: hot, cold, contact and pain. There are a number of different types of pressure receptor which detect variations in touch, and allow us to determine textures, etc. The hairs on the skin also play a role in our sensory perception.

Vitamin D Production

One of the most exciting things (well, for a nerd like me at least) that the skin does is actively manufacture vitamin D upon exposure to ultraviolet rays from the sun. It does this by transforming cholesterol into vitamin D3, which is actually a precursor for the active form of this nutrient that requires further conversion by the liver and kidneys. This transformation of cholesterol takes place in two deep areas of the skin: the stratum basale and the stratum spinosum.

Structure of the Skin

A key to getting a healthy skin is understanding its structure and the complexities of how it works.

The Epidermis

The epidermis is the outermost layer of the skin; its thickness varies throughout the body. On the soles of the feet and the palms of the hands, the epidermis is around 1–5mm thick. In contrast, the eyelids have an epidermis of 0.5mm. The epidermis is made up of five distinct layers. These are:

- The stratum corneum (the very top layer)
- The stratum lucidum
- The stratum granulosum
- The stratum spinosum
- The stratum basale (the very bottom layer)

Each layer is made up of different types of cells. The top layer, the stratum corneum, is made up of flat, dead skin cells that regularly slough away and shed, on average, every two weeks. The bottom layer, the stratum basale, is where new skin cells begin to form. Most of this layer is made up of cells that resemble columns, which push other growing cells upwards into the other layers of the skin, where they move through the ranks until they reach the stratum corneum, where they are eventually sloughed away.

There are also several types of specialist cell found within the epidermis. The first of these are the melanocytes. These are the cells responsible for giving our skin its pigment (melanin) and its lovely summer tan. They are located in the stratum basale, and secrete melanin in response to various stimuli, the main one being exposure to ultraviolet radiation. When melanocytes secrete melanin, they transport it to keratinocytes through a network of dendrites. At its destination, the melanin gives dark coloration to the skin.

The next group of specialized cells in the epidermis are the Langerhans cells. These are involved in identifying potentially pathogenic organisms, and sending signals to other branches of the immune system, as a kind of skin-bound early warning mechanism.

The final group of specialized cells in the epidermis are called merkel cells, but strangely we are yet to discover exactly what they do!

The Dermis

The dermis is the next layer down in the skin's structure. It can be anywhere between 10 and 40 times thicker than the epidermis. The very top part of the dermis is a rocky, bumpy terrain consisting of projections of fibres, blood vessels and nerve endings. This upper layer that meets the epidermis is known as the dermal papillae. The main type of cell that is found in the dermis is a cell called a fibroblast. The role of this busy cell is the constant manufacture and secretion of the two key structural components of the skin – collagen and elastin. These fibrous protein filaments give the skin its plumpness, firmness and elasticity. These cells are found mostly in the very upper layer of the dermis, in the region of the dermal papillae.

The lower part of the dermal papillae is home to a series of micro capillaries. Some of these vessels are found lower down in the dermis too. Their role is to provide oxygen and nutrients to the epidermis, and also to regulate the skin's temperature.

Below the dermal papillae, the deeper parts of the dermis are known as the reticular dermis. This thick tissue, with many criss-crossing collagen and elastin fibres, is also home to the pilosebaccous unit. This structure consists of a hair, the hair follicle, a sebaceous gland and the musculature used to make hairs stand up and relax. It delivers lubrication to the skin in the form of sebum – the oily secretion released by the sebaceous gland. You will see later in this book that this can be the site of some problems. Sweat glands are also found in the reticular dermis, along with a series of ducts that carry sweat up to the dermis during thermoregulation.

The Subcutis

The subcutis, often called the hypodermis, or subcutaneous layer, is the deepest and thickest part of the skin. This region is composed predominantly of collagen fibres and fat storage cells known as adipocytes. These fatty cells are grouped together in clumps within this layer. The fats contained within the subcutis not only offer a certain degree of cushioning to us, but also work as an energy source. It is in this area that we accumulate body fat, from sedentary living or over consumption of the wrong types of foods. These fats can be put back into circulation as fuel when we are following a weight-management diet or are exercising effectively.

A high number of cells from the immune system, known as macrophages, are also found within the subcutis. These cells are able to identify any pathogens or dysfunctional cells from our body, and completely engulf them. Once they have engulfed them, they quickly break down the invader or damaged cell and remove it rapidly. This is a crude but effective first-line defence.

The subcutis is also home to some other larger structures. There is a series of thicker blood vessels that supply the smaller capillaries that run through the dermis. Bundled in with these is a series of lymphatic vessels that lead from the other two layers of the skin. These vessels carry away waste material created from normal metabolic processes, plus they can filter out some pathogenic material too.

The final group of structures housed in the subcutis are the nerve structures. Nervous tissue runs throughout all the layers of the skin, with the nerve endings being at the very top of the epidermis in order to allow us to touch and feel the world around us. The subcutis is where this nervous tissue begins to bundle together, plus there are some unique neurological structures that reside here, including the pacinian corpuscle. This is actually a type of nerve receptor that detects pressure and vibration.

2
How the Skin Ages

The natural ageing of the skin is an inevitable process. I'm sorry to break that news to you. However, there is a lot that we can do to at least slow things down and make the best we can with the genes we have got. It is therefore important, now we are familiar with the skin's structure, to get an idea as to how it ages.

Ageing of the Epidermis

One of the first things to occur in the ageing epidermis is a reduction in melanocytes. These are the cells that secrete colour pigment within the skin when we are exposed to ultraviolet radiation, as part of the skin's protective mechanism against radiation mediated damage. As the number of melanocytes begins to decline, the upper layers of the skin are less able to create enough of the protective pigment melanin. This, of course, puts the skin at greater risk of ultraviolet damage, which can lead to localized free radical formation, not to mention increasing susceptibility to skin cancer.

The immunological cells known as Langerhans cells also start to decrease in number, which potentially reduces the barrier function of the skin against pathogens.

The main thing that people often notice as their skin ages is a dullness and change in colour and tone. This is largely due to the fact that this upper layer of the skin is losing nutrition as it ages. Because the epidermis doesn't have its own specific blood supply, it gleans oxygen and nutrients from the dermis. As the skin ages, contact between the dermis and epidermis begins to diminish, and as such the delivery of these vital components reduces, which will lead to poor cellular function in this upper layer. The end result is dull and lifeless skin.

The final assault on the epidermis is that it naturally begins to thin. This is because the rapid turnover of skin cells described in the previous chapter begins to slow down, and by our 70s it is 50 per cent less than in our 20s. This makes the skin look sunken and even saggy in places.

Ageing of the Dermis

Ageing has a great effect on the dermis. The fibroblast cells that are responsible for the formation of collagen begin to shrivel, reducing the amount of collagen that is manufactured. Remember that collagen and elastin, plus the extracellular matrix, are the fundamental structures that enable the skin to maintain elasticity, and to maintain its youthful structure. Existing collagen also begins to thin out, as there is a notable rise in enzymes called metalloproteinases that are responsible for breaking down collagen. Therefore its elasticity and structural capabilities begin to diminish.

The dermis is the area that houses most of the skin's blood supply. As we age there is a notable reduction in blood vessels, and circulation to this area is reduced. This will cause an obvious reduction in the amount of oxygen and nutrients that are delivered here. This is the main reason why ageing skin begins to look pale, and even feel colder – simply because there is less blood flow to the area.

These two processes see the whole density of the dermis decrease notably during ageing.

Ageing of the Subcutaneous Layer

This thick fatty layer that consists mainly of fat and collagen fibres will also thin out. The levels of fat in this area will begin to reduce, giving less fullness to the skin. This notably affects thermoregulation, as natural insulation begins to reduce.

Factors Influencing Skin Ageing

Free Radical Damage

The most widely understood factor in the ageing of all tissues is the free radical ageing theory. Free radicals are highly reactive molecules that are produced during metabolic processes in the body. I won't go too deeply into free radicals at this point, as they are explained in greater detail in Chapter 6 on Antioxidants. Basically, they are chemically unbalanced molecules that are desperately seeking an electron to make them chemically stable. They really aren't fussy blighters at all. They will nick one from anywhere. They collide into cells and barge in and steal electrons at any given opportunity. This collision causes the cells in tissues to become damaged. Free radicals can also cause damage to the DNA code of a cell which will affect the way in which it reproduces. This can result in tissues slowly degrading as their genetic code becomes more obscured. As tissues become more greatly affected in such a way, they are in essence ageing.

Some of these free radicals are produced naturally by the body during normal processes, whereas others are produced as the body metabolizes and deals with environmental factors. This type of free radical arrives from behaviour such as smoking, drinking to excess, eating fried foods, pollution, etc. Dealing with excessive free radicals involves lifestyle choices and a broad intake of antioxidants over a lifetime (see Chapter 6 for an in-depth look into this).

Collagen Cross Linking

One element that is not discussed anywhere near as widely as it should be is the impact that our high carbohydrate modern Western diet will have upon the ageing of the skin. Apart from this diet obviously being devoid of micronutrients and antioxidants, and being high in free-radical-forming components, it is also causing havoc to our blood sugar.

This type of diet is packed with refined carbohydrates: white rice, white bread, white pasta, fizzy drinks, ready meals, snack bars, etc. It's a diet full of simple sugars. The problem with these types of sugar is that they enter our blood stream very rapidly indeed, which elevates our blood sugar dramatically. The body's response to this is to release the hormone insulin, which encourages cells in the body to suck up this sugar as rapidly as possible, because if blood sugar levels remain high it can be life threatening. Now, this process over time is linked to many lifestyle diseases, but that is outside the subject matter of this book. What you need to know here is that when there is a sudden rise in blood sugar, the skin doesn't get away untouched.

A type of reaction takes place called a glycation reaction. This causes a rigid material to "cross link" collagen and elastin fibres. This means it fuses the two together in such a way that they lose their ability to stretch, essentially making them brittle. This makes the skin lose elasticity rapidly and can soon result in wrinkles and furrows in the skin. The key here is to follow a low GI diet that is made up of wholefoods, i.e. the type of food recommended in this book!

3
Common Skin Conditions

The conditions outlined below are those that are most responsive to dietary intervention. There are hundreds of different skin conditions, but not all will respond to dietary treatment. Those that require more specialized dermatological treatment have been omitted.

General Considerations for the Management of Skin Disorders

While each skin disorder has its own unique set of circumstances that require bespoke management, there are some physiological elements that most of them share.

Managing Inflammation

Most common skin conditions will involve active inflammation at varying stages of their progression. Inflammation is a necessary part of the healing process and something that shouldn't be fully suppressed. It arises when cells within a certain tissue become aware of changes that have occurred in that particular tissue that may lead to damage or infection. Specific cells respond to this change by releasing chemical messengers that start the inflammatory process. These signals cause an increased blood flow to the affected area, which causes redness and heat (known as rubor and calor). This allows for a more rapid transport of oxygen, nutrients and immunological components, such as white blood cells, to the affected area. As the blood vessels widen to enhance circulation, the walls become slightly porous, which helps white blood cells move to the affected area with greater ease.

You can see how this is a necessary process for healing. However, it is this process that is responsible for the appearance of many skin lesions. Just think of the redness and heat of the early stages of an eczema flare-up, or the red anger of a newly formed acne spot. One of the keys to dietary management of skin conditions is to consume food that creates an environment for inflammation to be kept to a minimum. This could involve manipulating our intake of dietary fats, or focusing on groups of specific nutrients.

Improving Skin Cell Function

Another key area of managing skin conditions via dietary means is supplying the body with the necessary nutrients to improve the health of the skin cells, making the tissue function better as a whole. I know this sounds a little generic, but improving overall skin function can often be a better approach than trying to target specific physiological processes too directly.

There are two main ways in which diet can influence overall skin tissue health. Firstly, it can influence the skin's ability to retain and utilize moisture. Providing adequate nutrients will keep cell membranes nice and fluid and supple.

Secondly, diet regulates the rate of skin cell turnover. Several nutrients play a direct role in this. If the layers of the skin are being shed too slowly that may contribute to the formation of blackheads (comedones); if they are shed too rapidly, that may lead to scaling in psoriasis lesions. Providing the correct nutrients will help the cells to start to behave closer to what is normal.

The Conditions

Acne Vulgaris

Acne has got to be one of the most distressing conditions that anyone can suffer from, especially when it is on the face – that part of our body that is constantly on show. It is a condition that I can relate to very well and is the reason I sit here today writing this book and working in the natural health industry.

Acne has quite a simple cause: too much sebum (oil) is released from the skin's sebaceous glands; or the sebum has an increased viscosity; or there's a combination of the two.

The two most widely affected areas for acne are the face and the back where the highest concentrations of pilosebaceous units are found. Each unit consists of a hair follicle, a sebaceous gland and a hair.

The sebaceous glands begin to enlarge and produce higher volumes of sebum when there is an elevation of androgen (i.e. testosterone). A rise in androgen can occur for a whole host of reasons. Most commonly it is as a result of puberty, and in young males. However, there are other causes such as hormonal fluctuations when a woman is using the contraceptive pill, or comes off the pill. It can also occur in cases of polycystic ovarian syndrome, where ovarian follicles are not functioning correctly and are releasing higher than normal levels of androgen.

There are several stages in the development of an acne lesion. The first involves small changes within the pilosebaceous unit. The increased production of sebum causes the pore to fill with oil rather rapidly. This then traps dead skin cells that naturally slough off the skin's surface on a daily basis. These cells, along with sebum, and a protein called keratin, can begin to form a plug within the pore, leading to an initial blockage. This blockage then prevents sebum from exiting the pore and lubricating the skin. This can cause a natural reflex of an increase in sebum production. This early stage of formation is called a comedone (blackhead).

The next stage is an increase in bacterial numbers within the blocked vessel. The bacterium *Propionibacterium acnes* (*P. acnes*) naturally lives happily within the pore, but isn't prominent enough to create any issues in the local tissue that would lead to infection. The *P. acnes* bacterium actually uses sebum as a food source. When sebum production increases, it is logical that the number of bacteria will also begin to rise within the blocked pore. As the pore continues to fill with sebum, bacteria and cells etc, inflammation begins, and the red bump that we associate with the first signs of a spot starts to appear.

The following stage may or may not occur. If sufficient pressure is able to build up within the pore, then the sides of the actual pore can rupture, causing its contents to leak into the surrounding skin. This will allow the bacteria to cause infection in the area. This is when the immune system starts to intervene. White blood cells from the immune system begin to rush to the area in order to deal with the infection. As these white cells attack the bacteria and destroy them, they themselves die off. The accumulation of these dead white cells forms pus, which soon begins to fill the pore. Hence a white head is formed.

Top Acne-fighting Nutrients

Vitamin A – regulates sebaceous secretions and improves skin tone.

Vitamin C – while this nutrient seems to have gained a certain panacea/cure-all status for virtually every condition, it certainly does have an important role to play in fighting infection and wound-healing. A little extra vitamin C will help active infected acne lesions heal a little faster, will help in scar-tissue formation, and also give the immune system a little support.

Zinc – regulates the way in which androgen hormones influence the sebaceous glands, reducing excessive sebum production. Zinc also helps in wound-healing because it regulates the activity of white blood cells that fight the bacterial infection.

Omega 3 Fatty Acids – these are probably the best nutrients to reduce the appearance of, and speed up the healing time of, active acne lesions. This is because they help the body to manufacture its own intrinsic anti-inflammatory compounds called prostaglandins. These are by-products produced in the body from metabolizing dietary fatty acids, and are involved in the management of the inflammatory response. Omega 3 fatty acids enable us to produce the types of prostaglandin that actually reduce inflammation, so can help to rapidly reduce the redness and swelling of an active spot.

Fat-soluble Antioxidants – are vital for helping to manage inflammation in any active skin lesions. This is because there is a certain percentage of the inflammatory response that is instigated

by a localized free radical release by white blood cells, so additional antioxidants will help to buffer this. The fat-soluble antioxidants are the only ones that can deliver this activity through dietary consumption alone. These are compounds such as the carotenoids (beta carotene, alpha carotene, etc), which will naturally begin to make their way into the upper layers of the skin where they can deliver their activity.

Top Acne-fighting Foods

Pumpkin Seeds – great source of zinc and essential fatty acids.
Prawns (Shrimps) – great source of zinc, selenium and the powerful carotenoid astaxanthin.
Red (Bell) Peppers – source of anti-inflammatory beta carotene.
Sweet Potatoes – rich source of beta carotene, plus immunomodulating proteins to help support immune function.

Foods to Avoid

Sugary Foods

I have read many an article that says that there is no link between sugary foods, such as sweets and chocolate, and spots. However, I personally disagree with this, and here's why.

Sugar is in essence a stimulant when taken in its refined form. When we eat large amounts of refined sugar at one sitting (i.e. a chocolate bar), our body has to get this sugar out of the bloodstream as soon as possible, as it can cause damage to tissues if in circulation for too long. The fastest way to do this is to tell cells to suck it in and use it for energy. The body does this by releasing a surge of insulin from the pancreas. The insulin instructs cells to take up the sugar.

However, when we get a large spike of adrenaline such as this, it also stimulates our adrenal glands, and causes us to release adrenaline, which helps our cells to use up a bit more of the sugar. The down side to this is that adrenaline directly stimulates the sebaceous glands within the skin. When these glands are stimulated, they will release more oil, and the risk of developing a comedone increases.

Eczema

Eczema is a condition that plagues millions, and one that seems to be becoming more common, especially among teens and young adults. It is reasonably common among small children as their bodies develop, but the number of people that go on to develop chronic eczema to early adulthood and beyond is rising at a rate of knots.

Eczema, in essence, is just an inflammation of the skin. There are some closely related skin conditions that come under the eczema bracket, such as contact dermatitis, that have been omitted for now, as the primary focus here is atopic eczema. *Atopic* means that there is a familial tendency toward acute allergic reactions, which can manifest itself in several ways, in the form of eczema, asthma and hay fever.

Eczema, asthma and hay fever are, believe it or not, exactly the same condition, just manifesting itself in different body tissues. We often find that individuals with one of the above have family members that suffer from one of the other atopic conditions, or themselves go on to develop one of the other conditions. These atopic conditions are what we refer to as a type 2 hypersensitivity reaction. This is where our own immune system has, for whatever reason, become overly sensitized to a specific stimulus.

Every time that our body is exposed to this specific stimulus (which could be food, a detergent, a cosmetic, anything), our immune system automatically recognizes it as a pathological influence, and instigates an immunological response to it. This causes a localized immunological reaction that can lead to inflammation and redness. As there is an allergic element to this condition, antibodies to the specific stimulus are created. There is also a localized release of histamine by a type of white blood cell called a mast cell. When histamine begins to accumulate locally, this will bring on the intense itching that so many eczema sufferers report.

Symptoms of Eczema

Redness

The redness that is experienced in the early stages of an eczema flare-up is active inflammation in action. When the immune system realizes that we have been exposed to the particular irritant that affects us, it quickly recruits lots of white blood cells, and sends them off to the skin. When these blood cells arrive at the skin, they leach out chemicals that cause the blood vessels to open rapidly, giving a redness to the skin. This widening of the blood vessels allows the white blood cells to move into tissues more rapidly. When they widen in such a manner, they also allow some of the watery portion of the blood, the plasma, to leach out into surrounding tissue. This causes the swelling that accompanies redness when inflammation is active.

Dry Skin

Many eczema sufferers experience dry skin. This occurs as a secondary result of the inflammatory events during the early stages of a flare-up. When this happens, it can affect circulation to the sebaceous glands, reduce levels of sebum in the skin, and also cause a water loss from the cell. This leads to skin that is dry and shriveled, and quick to flake off.

The dry flaky appearance of the skin is also accelerated by a more rapid dying of skin cells, due to damage from inflammatory episodes. The skin cells are stretched and affected in a multitude of ways during the inflammatory response, to such a degree that they will stop functioning normally. In the light of this, they simply die off faster than usual, causing a flaky appearance.

Itching

One of the most distressing symptoms of eczema is the chronic itching that accompanies a flare-up. The itching is caused by the localized release of histamine by a mast cell. As histamine accumulates in an area, it facilitates many chemical reactions locally, but also stimulates pain receptors in a specific way. When histamine stimulates nociceptors (pain receptors at nerve endings), the sensation experienced is an intense itching, which can drive sufferers to distraction.

Top Eczema-fighting Nutrients

Essential Fatty Acids – These vital nutrients have several important roles to play in the management of eczema. Firstly, and most superficially, they help the skin to retain more moisture by enhancing the fluidity of skin cell membranes.

The most important application of essential fatty acids, however, is to manage flare-ups. During the first stages of a flare-up, there is a huge amount of active inflammation taking place in the skin. The right types of fatty acids can help our body fight inflammation by allowing it to create its own natural anti-inflammatory compounds known as prostaglandins.

Prostaglandins are communication molecules that are by-products of the metabolism of dietary fats. There are three different types of prostaglandins: series 1, series 2 and series 3. Series 2 prostaglandins are used by the body to activate and enhance inflammation, and to increase pain signalling. Series 1 and series 3 prostaglandins, on the other hand, are used by the body to turn off inflammation, and reduce pain signalling.

Different types of dietary fats will influence the production of different types of prostaglandin. Saturated animal fats, for example, such as that found in red meat, etc, will be metabolized to form the series 2 prostaglandins that actually exacerbate inflammation and pain.

In contrast, omega 3 fatty acids, such as those found in oily fish and some types of seeds, will increase the production of series 1 and series 3 prostaglandins – those natural anti-inflammatories.

By manipulating our intake of certain types of dietary fats, we can influence what type of prostaglandins are produced, and play a notable role in controlling inflammation naturally.

B Vitamins – are among the most important nutrients for the health of the skin, as they support it on so many levels. As a group, they will support the microcirculation to the outer layers of the skin, which helps to ensure adequate delivery of oxygen and nutrients to the skin, and also carry away waste products from skin cells. This activity has the added bonus of improving skin tone and pigmentation.

The B vitamins are also involved in regulating the turnover of skin cells, and can help to reduce flakiness. They help with the proper metabolism and utilization of essential fatty acids, so a good intake is important when consuming extra fatty acids of any kind.

Fat-soluble Antioxidants – such as beta carotene, and certain flavonoids can be of great use in managing any type of inflammatory skin lesion, for the simple fact they deliver localized antioxidant activity. Some aspects of the inflammatory response are instigated by the local release of free radicals from white blood cells. Adding some antioxidants can help to buffer this to a certain degree. However, it is important that we select the right types of antioxidant in order to achieve this. We need to consume antioxidants that are fat-soluble so that they will make their way into the skin (see the Antioxidants chapter for more details). The ideal group for this is the carotenoids. These are the compounds that give foods such as carrots, sweet potatoes and mangoes their vivid orange colour.

Other Remedies of Interest

While the main focus of this book is how eating the right food can help the skin, I'm going to put on my herbalist's hat for a moment and discuss two other remedies that are in my experience extremely valuable for the management of eczema.

Chickweed Cream/Ointment

Chickweed is a common garden weed that has been used in herbal medicine for centuries. It is a very powerful anti-pruritic. This means that it reduces itching. It also has a notable anti-inflammatory activity. The cream or ointment can be applied as and when needed. It's certainly a great alternative to slapping on endless coats of emollient cream.

Reishi Mushroom

This remedy is one of the most exciting natural remedies for any of the atopic triangle (asthma, eczema, hay fever), and I have seen dramatic results. Reishi mushroom is a type of woody tree fungus that is native to Europe, Asia and the USA. It has the ability to influence the immune system in a very profound manner. Remember that, in atopic issues such as asthma, eczema and hay fever, the body's immune system begins to develop antibodies to a specific stimulus (pollen, dust mite, cosmetic, etc). Whenever this stimulus is experienced, then an immunological response is instigated, and symptoms arise.

Now, here we get to the exciting bit. Our immune system has two distinct branches to it. These are antibody-mediated responses and non-specific responses.

Antibody-mediated responses involve the body's ability to recognize specific pathogens and harmful stimuli. When this recognition takes place, the immune system knows exactly what kind of immunological response to deliver in order to deal with that particular invader. This branch of the immune system develops throughout our lives, and is the basis upon which immunizations work. Every time it comes across it, the immune system knows how to react.

The other branch of the immune system is the non-specific branch. This is the branch that we are born with. It doesn't have the ability to recognize a specific invader. Instead, it can recognize whether something belongs to the body or comes from outside. It can also recognize whether a cell in the body has become infected, by specific markers that an infected cell displays upon its outer surface. The problem with this is that people who suffer

from atopic type conditions tend to have a slightly over-active antibody-mediated response, which needs calming down a little bit. This is where things begin to get exciting. These two branches of the immune system are mutually inhibitory, meaning that when one branch is activated, the other is automatically switched off. The two cannot be active at the same time.

Reishi mushroom can remedy this situation due to a fascinating interaction with the immune system. Reishi mushroom contains a very large sugar molecule called a polysaccharide. This sugar has an interaction with areas of tissue in the gut known as Peyer's patches. These patches of tissue work almost like surveillance stations, constantly sampling gut contents for any potential invaders or pathogens, and relaying this information back to the rest of the immune system, so the immune system knows which type of attack to deliver to any potential invader. When the polysaccharides from reishi mushroom pass over the Peyer's patches, they set off an alarm response. This is because they are similar in shape to polysaccharides displayed on the outer surfaces of certain types of bacteria. As they move across the Peyer's patches, the cells within the patches think that the body is coming under a certain type of attack, and ring the alarm. The end result of this is that we get an upsurge in non-specific type immune responses.

If you cast your mind back, you will recall that each of these immunological responses is mutually inhibitory. When one is activated, the other is switched off. So, as reishi mushroom polysaccharides cause an upsurge in non-specific immune responses, antibody-mediated responses will be turned down. Remember that eczema occurs because the immune system has developed an antibody to a specific stimulus – the very type of antibody-mediated response that reishi dumbs down. I have seen this remedy work wonders in a matter of weeks. Available in capsule or tablet form, it is really worth trying.

Top Eczema-fighting Foods

Oily Fish – packed to the hilt with inflammation-busting omega 3 fatty acids.
Brown Rice – full of B vitamins.
Sweet Potatoes – full of the potent fat-soluble antioxidant beta carotene.
Flax Seeds and Pumpkin Seeds – both rich sources of essential fatty acids.

Erythema Nodosum

Erythema nodosum is a painful inflammatory skin disorder that affects the fatty layer of the skin. It presents itself as very tender red smooth nodules on the shins, trunk, thighs, face and neck. It is a lesion that often is short lived and follows some other type of physiological event, and is essentially a transient hypersensitivity reaction.

As it is a semi-acute, self-limiting condition, there is nothing from a dietary perspective that can be done to prevent the condition, but there is certainly a lot that can be done from a treatment point of view. Heavy consumption of the right kind of foods can notably increase healing time.

Top Erythema Nodosum-fighting Nutrients

Essential Fatty Acids – yes, fatty acids again. I can't emphasize strongly enough how important these nutrients are for managing any kind of inflammatory issues, be they in the skin or anywhere else in the body. A good intake of fatty acids will help erythema nodosum lesions to ease just that little bit faster.

Fat-soluble Antioxidants – such as beta carotene, can help with inflammatory issues. However, as these antioxidants are fat-soluble, and erythema nodosum affects the fatty layer of the skin, their consumption becomes even more relevant. As fat-soluble compounds, these antioxidants will begin to naturally migrate into this fatty layer of the skin. It is here that they may help to buffer some of the inflammatory activity. Some elements of the inflammatory response involve a localized release of free radicals, so extra targeted antioxidants can make a big difference to the severity of the lesion.

Top Erythema Nodosum-fighting Foods

Sweet Potatoes, Carrots, Mangoes – all rich sources of the fat-soluble antioxidant beta carotene.

Oily Fish, Nuts and Seeds – rich sources of essential fatty acids.

Whole Grains – such as brown rice, to provide extra B vitamins for optimal skin tissue health.

Keratosis Pilaris

Keratosis pilaris is a condition that I see a lot – not only with clients, but also when I'm out and about, and I bet you have too. It displays itself as small sandpapery reddish pink bumps, most commonly found on the backs of the arms but it also appears on the thighs and buttocks. Affected areas can turn darker sometimes too. It often can worsen during pregnancy and does have a tendency to improve with age.

Keratosis pilaris has similarities with one of the early stages of acne. This is the blockage of a hair follicle with keratin, a protein in the skin. This blockage then causes pressure to build within the follicle, and the contents bulge out, creating the little bumps.

Top Keratosis Pilaris-fighting Nutrients

Vitamin A – the most important nutrient when it comes to managing keratin production. If too much keratin is being produced too quickly, or if not enough is being produced, then additional vitamin A in the diet can help to regulate this. Reducing any excessive keratin production can notably decrease the severity of keratosis pilaris lesions.

B Vitamins – are great from virtually every aspect of skin health. They are of particular use in regulating the turnover of skin cells. Apart from excessive keratin in the hair follicle, the other factor that contributes to the formation of these bumps is blockage with dead skin cells. If we are shedding them too quickly, this may aggravate the process. Extra B vitamins can help to regulate the turnover of cells.

Lichen Planus

Lichen planus is a condition that is inflammatory in origin. It affects the arms, legs, scalp, mouth and mucous membranes of the vagina. Its exact cause still remains something of a mystery, although it is understood that it is not infectious, doesn't run in families, and cannot be passed to others. It is a non-specific inflammatory lesion.

It appears as small, multi-sided bumps that grow together in clumps, that can develop scaly areas. The one thing unique to lichen planus, that makes it distinctive from other similar lesions such as eczema and psoriasis, is its notorious lilac/violet colour.

Top Lichen Planus-fighting Nutrients

Essential Fatty Acids – the firm favourites for tackling any kind of inflammatory condition. They are beneficial because they help the body to create its own natural anti-inflammatory compounds.

Selenium – some empirical data suggests that increased selenium intake can have beneficial effects upon the severity of lichen planus lesions. This is most likely due to production of antioxidant enzymes which help to reduce the severity of inflammation.

Top Foods for Lichen Planus

Oily Fish, Flax Seeds, Hemp Seeds – packed with anti-inflammatory fatty acids.

Brazil Nuts – packed with selenium. Just three Brazil nuts a day can give the full Recommended Daily Allowance (RDA) of selenium.

Psoriasis

Psoriasis is another of the relatively common skin disorders, affecting in the region of 2 per cent of the population. There is no pattern with regards to age or sex.

Psoriasis is a condition that affects the rate of turnover of skin cells. As was discussed in the previous chapter, new skin cells are formed at the very bottom layer of the skin, and gradually move outwards as different layers of the skin shed dead cells. The new cells reach the upper layer in around 3 to 4 weeks. However, in cases of psoriasis, this whole sequence is moving at light speed. New cells that get formed in the lower layers of the skin will rise up and be shed in as little as 3 to 4 days.

There is a new chain of thought now that believes this condition arises as a result of a default in the immune system, where the system sends out a message that causes this increased cellular turnover. This theory involves a group of white blood cells called T cells that migrate to the dermis, and release a series of chemical messengers called cytokines that cause a localized inflammation, which in turn will cause a more rapid dying off and turnover of skin cells.

The psoriasis lesion appears as haphazard patches of redness, with a silvery coloured flaky scaliness in the centre.

Top Psoriasis-fighting Nutrients

Essential Fatty Acids – These beauties come up a lot in this book, and rightly so. They are one of the most profound groups of nutrients for both maintenance of skin health and also the treatment of many common skin conditions. In psoriasis, regardless of whether the immunological theory is correct, there is certainly an inflammatory involvement. This can be observed during a flare-up, where the patches of redness are formed. This redness indicates active inflammation. The essential fatty acids, especially omega 3, help the body to create its own natural anti-inflammatory compounds, the prostaglandins, which can aid in the reduction of the redness that accompanies psoriasis. While this doesn't necessarily stop the condition from arising in the first place, it certainly offers some considerable benefit in the management of its symptoms.

The other benefit to increasing essential fatty acid intake is that it will help to keep the skin more moist. One of the factors in psoriasis is the dry flakiness of the skin in the centre of the lesions. While this is caused by accelerated skin cell turnover, its appearance can be reduced a little by making the skin able to retain moisture better – an effect delivered by essential fatty acids. This is another step in managing the appearance and severity of lesions.

Quercetin – is a powerful bioflavonoid compound that has commonly been used for conditions such as hay fever and allergies.

However, new findings suggest that it may have a role to play in inflammatory skin lesions. This is because quercetin inhibits an enzyme in the body called phospholipase. This enzyme is involved in the production of a fatty acid derivative called arachidonic acid. As mentioned earlier, a group of communication molecules called prostaglandins is involved in regulating the inflammatory response. Some prostaglandins switch inflammation on, whereas others switch it off. Arachidonic acid is responsible for the formation of the type of prostaglandins that switch on inflammation. Therefore, inhibiting arachidonic acid will reduce the presence of pro-inflammatory prostaglandins and aid in the reduction in appearance of inflammatory skin lesions.

B Vitamins – again, another favourite in any skin condition. These become especially important in psoriasis, as one of their roles is the regulation of skin cell turnover. It is believed by many practitioners that adequate B vitamin intake can slow down skin cell turnover in psoriasis patients.

The most important of the B vitamins here is folate, which is directly associated with skin cell turnover, although the other B vitamins offer support in this context too. While the evidence for this remains unclear, what is certain is that adequate B vitamin intake can certainly improve the overall appearance of the lesions, and also improve skin tone overall.

Top Psoriasis-fighting Foods

Garlic – contains a compound that inhibits lipoxygenase, another enzyme involved in arachidonic acid activity.
Red Onions – a rich source of quercetin.
Oily Fish, Nuts and Seeds – great sources of essential fatty acids.
Whole Grains – such as brown rice, are a rich source of B vitamins.

Other Remedies of Interest

Vitamin D Creams

These have become more and more popular in both natural and conventional treatment of psoriasis. Research has found that vitamin D increases the binding of a peptide (communication protein) called cathelicidin to DNA, which causes a notable inhibition of the specific inflammatory response involved in the instigation of psoriasis lesions. Research is in its early days and there is still little clarity as to whether dietary vitamin D will interact with the condition in the same way. But it is food for thought.

Rosacea

Rosacea is another distressing skin condition that while not medically serious can cause a huge amount of personal problems, due to the fact that it affects the face. It is characterized by facial redness, sometimes with the addition of small spots. Some cases also involve permanent dilation of blood vessels in affected areas. In some very advanced cases, lobules can form on the nose, giving a bumpy, even bulbous appearance.

There have been several different causative factors linked with the development of rosacea, all of which seem to be plausible. It is therefore likely that each of these influences will create an environment or biological scenario that will allow the condition to develop.

Skin Flushing

One of the major factors believed to instigate rosacea is prolonged flushing of the skin. This can be caused by a variety of factors such as exposure to varying temperatures (going from cold to hot very rapidly), regular heavy exercise, and even excessive alcohol consumption. All of these lead to vascular changes and dilation of blood vessels. Usually the blood vessels return to normal in a matter of minutes, but continual fluctuations in vessel sizes, and the strain this places upon the musculature of the vessel walls, can lead to permanent dilation of the vessel.

Intestinal Bacteria

There is now a clear link between disturbances in gut bacteria composition and rosacea. Recent studies have used the hydrogen breath test where a positive test result indicates the overgrowth of bad bacteria within the small intestine. Patients with rosacea were more often hydrogen positive than those patients in the trial who did not suffer from the condition. When these patients were treated with antibiotics, their rosacea symptoms cleared rapidly. The exact link between the bacterial overgrowth and the onset of rosacea symptoms is not 100 per cent clear, but certainly highlights an interesting therapeutic approach. See recommendations below.

Top Rosacea-fighting Nutrients

Essential Fatty Acids – as some cases of rosacea incorporate a certain amount of inflammatory activity, especially if any spots or pimples are present. The essential fatty acids, especially of the omega 3 variety, will help the body to create its own natural anti-inflammatory compounds, which can help to reduce the severity of these lesions.

B Vitamins – as with other skin conditions, B vitamins play a vital part in the management of rosacea. This is because they help to maintain the day-to-day functionality of the skin. They regulate everything from microcirculation to the outer layers, to the turnover of skin cells.

Probiotic Bacteria – these probably represent one of the most exciting natural approaches to treatment of this condition. As discussed above, there is a link between the overgrowth of certain types of bad bacteria in the small intestine and rosacea. While antibiotic treatments have proved successful in the past, it is my belief that such medications should only be used in conditions that are life-threatening, such as sepsis or acute infection, unless there really is no other option. Instead, one of the most powerful, safe and natural ways of dealing with such overgrowths is to ensure that we have a very healthy gut flora, by providing ample amounts of the good bacteria that live in our gut. These good bacteria offer a million and one beneficial effects to our health, from regulating the activity of gut tissue, to offering a physical barrier from pathogenic organisms, to regulating localized and systemic immune responses.

Good bacteria in the gut are the first line of defence if any other types of bacteria decide to try their luck and cause problems within our digestive tract. They soon wipe the bad bacteria out and make sure they don't go anywhere they are not supposed to. Regular supplementation with probiotic cultures and following a diet that is rich in prebiotic compounds (see below) are recommended.

Top Foods for Rosacea

Oily Fish – high in omega 3 fatty acids.
Red Onions – these contain a prebiotic agent, inulin, that encourages the growth of good bacteria.
Simply Cooked Dishes – too much spice and seasoning can cause excessive flushing.
Brightly Coloured Fruit and Vegetables – these bright colour pigments generally represent antioxidant compounds.

Foods to Avoid

Spicy Foods

In some individuals, rosacea is caused or aggravated by facial flushing. Some spicy foods can cause this rather rapidly and, as a result, can worsen the condition.

Chillies, for example, contain a powerful chemical called capsaicin – the stuff that actually burns your tongue. This compound can interact with the smooth muscle walls of the blood vessels, and cause them to relax. This leads to a rapid widening of the vessel, which will, in turn, cause a stimulation of circulation/flushing.

Ginger is another spice that can have this effect. The spicy essential oils in ginger that give it its flavour will have a similar effect to chillies as they cause relaxation of the blood vessels and the accompanying flushing.

4
Vital Vitamins

Vitamins are one of the most vital and also misunderstood aspects of skincare; one that we should all make ourselves familiar with, if we want clear vibrant skin.

If I were to ask, "What exactly do vitamins do?", how many of us would be able to give a direct answer? Very few I should imagine. That is because we have all been bombarded with huge amounts of media information about the next wonder vitamin, and how X vitamin may cause or cure Y condition. However, most people have little idea what these little gems actually do for us in the general sense.

Put as simply as is possible, vitamins are facilitators of biochemical events in the body. There are millions of biochemical chain reactions happening in our bodies every second. Different metabolic processes change one compound into another, in order to allow it to undertake a certain function. Different chemical pathways process hormones, create communication chemicals that send messages between cells and tissues, process dietary substances, the list goes on. Virtually all of these processes will require vitamins in certain levels in order for the chemical events to take place. So, it's clear to see that these are vital compounds and that notable deficiency of them can cause serious illness.

It is a sad fact that the foods that dominate in the Western world of convenience and haste are often completely devoid of vitamins. They are commonly packed to the hilt with macro nutrients such as fat, carbohydrates and protein, but micronutrients, such as vitamins, minerals and trace elements, have been lost in the mass production process. As so many of us are consuming such a diet, it's no wonder that skin problems are becoming more common.

The simplest way around this is to abandon the nasty ready meals that require a few pricks from a fork and 10 minutes being nuked in a microwave, and instead reach for fresh, unadulterated, wholesome ingredients. I can already hear the sighs of dismay from many readers, but fear not, in the pages that follow I will show you how affordable, easy and fun it is to prepare fresh foods for yourself.

Here's a brief outline of what does what when it comes to vitamins and your skin.

Vitamin A

Vitamin A is one nutrient that has a long history of therapeutic use in skin conditions. There are two main forms of vitamin A: retinol and beta carotene.

The retinoid form of this nutrient has been used by dermatologists in topical preparations, for the treatment of conditions such as acne, lichen planus and psoriasis. These are all conditions that are associated with an increase in the production of keratin. This is a protein within the skin which, if produced to excess within the skin, can cause blockage of pores, and an increased turnover of skin cells. Vitamin A is also known to help

support skin structures, such as collagen, which can help to reduce excessive wrinkling of the skin. The animal form of vitamin A, known as retinol, is found in abundance in foods such as red meat, liver, eggs and some cheeses.

The plant form of vitamin A, known as beta carotene, is the compound that delivers bright orange colour pigments to food that it is found in. Great examples of this are carrots, pumpkins, mangoes, etc. Beta carotene is a very potent antioxidant, that is fat-soluble, so can actually accumulate in the skin (see the antioxidant chapter for more details of this). This helps to provide a localized protection against free radical damage that can cause damage and degradation of collagen fibres, which in the long term can lead to wrinkling and reduced youthfulness of the skin, and a loss of fullness to the skin. A localized accumulation of carotenoids in the skin also gives the added benefit of delivering some localized anti-inflammatory activity, which can help to reduce the redness and physical appearance of skin lesions such as eczema flare-ups and acne breakouts. This is due to the antioxidant function of carotenoids. Several elements of the inflammatory response (that is highly active when you see redness on a skin lesion) are triggered by localized free radical release from white blood cells in normal response to the injury or infection, so adding some fat-soluble antioxidants to the mix is going to offer some protection against the free radical mediated inflammatory episodes.

Best Food Sources – eggs, liver, carrots, sweet potatoes, kale.

The B Vitamins

The B vitamins, as a group, are in my professional opinion one of the most important nutrients for overall skin health. The main emphasis in this book is on improving the skin's overall functioning as an organ from as many different angles as possible. No other group of nutrients supports the skin in such a diverse way as the B vitamins do. Each B vitamin supports different aspects of the skin's overall function. When put together, this allows for a far better, healthier functioning skin, and one that can only look better as a result. Here is a breakdown of the many ways in which these nutrients can benefit the skin:

B1 (Thiamin)

B1 is the nutrient to take if you want to give the skin a warm healthy glow. This is because B1 supports microcirculation to the layers of the skin. This is the bed of tiny capillaries that provide fresh blood, oxygen and nutrients to the skin. By encouraging better microcirculation in the skin, we allow for a better delivery of fresh oxygenated blood to the skin, plus a more effective removal of waste materials, and delivery of nutrients, thus helping the skin to meet its metabolic needs and function better generally. Plus, with improved circulation to the skin, we also get a nice glowing skin tone.

Best Food Sources – asparagus, mushrooms, spinach, sunflower seeds, green peas.

B2 (Riboflavin)

B2 doesn't particularly give any notable benefits when extra amounts are taken but a deficiency can leave your skin looking pretty grotty. When levels of this nutrient get too low, we see a dulling of the skin, along with patches of dryness. The most well known symptom of B2 deficiency, however, is angular stomatitis, which is a painful cracking in the corner of the mouth.

Best Food Sources – mushrooms, spinach, asparagus, broccoli, eggs.

B3 (Niacin)

B3 is a valuable nutrient for skin health, both from a maintenance perspective as well as from a therapeutic one. Its main role is in oxygenating the skin. It does this by acting as a vasodilator for the dermal microcirculation, which means that it forces the tiny network of blood vessels to widen, causing an increase in circulation to the upper layers of the skin. This helps with a number of activities, from wound healing to cellular function.

A word of caution, however. Many people find that this nutrient can cause a rapid and sometimes uncomfortable flushing of the skin. This creates patches of itchy redness. While this can be initially alarming, it is merely a demonstration that the nutrient is working. If you want a more subtle effect, you need to choose a different form of this nutrient. Commercially available forms of niacin come in two different chemical forms: nicotinic acid and niacinamide. The nicotinic acid form is the one that flushes the skin, whereas the niacinamide form delivers a much more gentle circulatory stimulation, without causing the pronounced flushing.

Best Food Sources – mushrooms, tuna, sea vegetables.

B5 (Pantothenic Acid)

B5 is used most commonly for individuals going through periods of intense stress, as it is involved in supporting the adrenal glands. However, it does have some application in skin health. It has frequently been used for treating itchy inflamed skin lesions such as eczema and contact dermatitis.

Best Food Sources – mushrooms, cauliflower, sunflower seeds, tomatoes, strawberries.

B6 (Pyridoxine)

B6 is an incredibly useful nutrient for the more aesthetic end of the skincare spectrum. It is closely involved in regulating the balance of sodium and potassium. As such, it has proved very helpful in the past for managing fluid accumulation in tissues, which makes it a useful nutrient to bear in mind for issues such as puffy eyes and a puffy face caused by fluid accumulation under the skin.

Best Food Sources – spinach, (bell) peppers, garlic, tuna, cauliflower, banana, celery, Brussels sprouts.

B12 (Cyanocobalamin)

B12 is predominantly used for red blood cell formation in the body. This can aid in oxygen transportation, plus it can give the skin a healthy glow. While not directly therapeutic, it is certainly a useful aid for making the skin look a little better.

Best Food Sources – liver, red snapper, prawns (shrimps), salmon, kelp, spirulina, tempeh, miso.

Vitamin C

Vitamin C has often been portrayed as one of those universal cure-alls that has benefits for almost every conceivable ailment.

It plays a vital role in the manufacture of collagen so, from a long-term perspective, it can be a useful nutrient to support a healthy ageing process, including the ageing of the skin. Collagen, the most abundant protein in the body, makes up about 25 per cent of all proteins in the body. Its primary roles are to maintain the rigidity and elasticity of connective tissues, and also to hold structures in place and to enable tissues to hold their structure. It is the job of vitamin C to link different parts of the molecule together as collagen is being constructed, so sufficient vitamin C intake can aid in the adequate manufacture of collagen.

Best Food Sources – citrus fruit, goji berries, spinach, red (bell) peppers.

Vitamin D

Vitamin D has become one of the most talked about nutrients of modern times. Barely a week goes by without it appearing in the world's press. There have been huge leaps in research recently that have highlighted the protective role that vitamin D plays in many

lifestyle diseases. There is also some evidence to suggest that vitamin D may be useful in the treatment and management of psoriasis. Skin cells have receptors for the active form of vitamin D (after it has been converted in the body), and vitamin D regulates the turnover of skin cells. As psoriasis is an over-accelerated turnover of skin cells, extra intake of this nutrient may well prove beneficial.

Best Food Sources – mushrooms, cheese, fish.

Vitamin E

Vitamin E is probably the most famous "skin nutrient" of all. It is a very well known antioxidant, of particular relevance to skin health. As it is fat-soluble, it can move into the fatty layers of the skin where it can offer maximum protection. In these layers there is a large proportion of collagen which gives the skin its structural integrity. The collagen here is susceptible to attack from free radicals, which in time can lead to wrinkling, dulled appearance of the skin, and a slower healing time for skin lesions. It will also make the skin look less plump and full.

There is another potential way that vitamin E is useful for the management of skin conditions. That is by supporting the immune system. In issues such as acne, there is obviously an infectious element. It is vital that we have a strong healthy immune system to be able to deal with the infection quickly and efficiently. Vitamin E protects the thymus gland (one of the main tissues involved in manufacturing white blood cells) and can also protect leukocytes (white cells) from damage during oxidative stress.

Best Food Sources – avocados, nuts, olive oil.

Food Preparation for Maximum Vitamin Intake

It's all well and good reaching for higher quality ingredients and fresh foods, but if they are cooked in the wrong way, or cooked to death, then much of the benefit that you hope to gain will sadly be lost. There are some simple rules to cooking fresh vegetables that will retain all of their goodness.

Most of the beneficial nutrients described above are in fact water-soluble substances. If you follow that age-old British tradition of boiling vegetables to within an inch of their life, then to be honest, you may as well throw the veggies away, and just drink the water. That's where all of the nutrients will be! As the nutrients are water-soluble, they will naturally want to leach out of the food and into the water. If you heat the water, this process will accelerate drastically, and you will be left with lifeless gloopy vegetables that taste hideous.

The cooking methods I favour are steaming and sautéing. Both retain most of the water-soluble nutrients (vitamin C, the B vitamins) in the food, not to mention the fact that sautéing especially brings the flavours of the food to life.

5

The Magic of Minerals

Minerals have to be the forgotten allies in the world of nutrition. This is especially true when it comes to skincare. Virtually everyone is familiar with the concept of calcium for healthy bones, and iron for energy. But how often do we consider minerals when we think of skin health? Certain minerals and trace elements have a huge role to play in both maintaining the day-to-day health of the skin, and also delivering a therapeutic benefit when tackling active conditions of the skin.

Chromium

Chromium is one mineral that may not immediately spring to mind when it comes to looking after the health of the skin. However, there is an indirect but vital link. One of the most destructive influences upon the health of the skin over a lifetime and the rate of skin ageing is continual blood sugar spikes. In our modern world of convenience and processed foods, we are consuming huge amounts of high glycaemic foods, such as white bread, white rice, white pasta, sugary drinks and snacks, etc. This means we are eating foods that release their sugar into our bloodstream very fast. We may feel that this gives us a quick energy boost, but it is actually rather harmful. Our blood sugar is not meant to rise rapidly. We are designed to be eating whole foods such as fruits, vegetables, nuts and seeds, etc. These foods release their sugars slowly and steadily. If our blood sugar rises rapidly, it is fraught with danger and as such we have a very rapid and effective way of dealing with such blood sugar spikes.

When our blood sugar rises, insulin is released from the pancreas. Insulin basically communicates to cells in our body, telling them to pull in sugar and convert it into energy. The faster our blood sugar rises, the greater the release of insulin. However, the insulin system can only deal with so much sugar at one time. Once we have passed the system's capacity to deal with any more sugar, the body does several things. It turns it into body fat, and also deposits it into other tissues.

It is when it becomes deposited into other tissues that trouble can start for the health of our skin. If excess sugar reaches the dermis, it can very quickly start to bond with collagen and elastin, in a process called glycation. Once the sugar has formed a permanent bond with collagen and elastin, it becomes an Advanced Glycation End product or AGE (which is rather appropriate). AGEs can then form further bonds with collagen and elastin, creating cross links between fibres. This causes the collagen lattice to become stiff, rather than elastic, which in turn leads to a loss in youthful skin elasticity, speeding up the ageing of the skin.

So, where does chromium fit into all of this? Well, chromium is used by the body to create something called Glucose Tolerance Factor (GTF). This molecule is involved in stabilizing blood sugar levels by working alongside insulin to further enhance a cell's ability to take in glucose effectively. It will help blood sugar to stay at a safe level for longer, which has a myriad of health benefits, but where the skin is concerned it means that there will be less likelihood that glucose will become deposited in the collagen matrix to form AGEs.

Best Food Sources – yeast, oysters, whole grains, potatoes.

Selenium

Selenium is a mineral that has been talked about a lot in recent years, and one that is still drastically deficient in the Western diet. It is a trace mineral, and as such is only required in tiny amounts, yet many of us still fail to consume enough. Part of this is due to the poor quality of soil in today's intensive farming. The more intensely land is farmed, the more its natural mineral content begins to decline. As the nutritional composition of fresh produce is a direct reflection of the soil in which it is grown, a lot of fresh produce today is lower in micronutrients than it was even 10 years ago. Couple this with poor food choices, and you soon see why our intake of such nutrients has declined to such an extent.

Selenium is a key player in long-term skin health. This is mostly due to its potent antioxidant promoting activity. Selenium is a cofactor (a substance necessary for the formation of another substance) in the production of a very powerful antioxidant enzyme called Glutathione Peroxidase (GP). GP plays a vital role in protecting cells and tissues from biochemical damage caused by free radicals. Glutathione Peroxidase that is formed in the presence of selenium can offer protection both to skin cells and also to the matrix of collagen fibres that offer support and structure to our skin. If these fibres become damaged in any way, due to free radical attack, or cross linking from insulin spiking, it can leave our skin looking dull and shallow, and make us much more susceptible to wrinkling earlier on in life.

The other benefit of selenium is the fact that it will deliver a certain amount of anti-inflammatory activity. This is again due to its antioxidant action. When a skin lesion, such as an acne spot or an eczema flare-up is red and angry, that means there is a lot of active localized inflammation. Part of the inflammatory response is enhanced by a localized free radical release (there are many steps involved in activating inflammation). Adding additional antioxidant nutrients and precursors can offer some benefit in the reduction of redness and severity of inflammatory lesions.

Best Food Sources – Brazil nuts, shiitake mushrooms, prawns (shrimps), tuna, sunflower seeds.

Silica

This wonderful mineral is one of the most important for long-term skin health, yet one which is seldom talked about outside of the healthfood world. Silica is found in a wide variety of fruits and vegetables. Its presence in a food often leads to the produce having a smooth shiny skin. Think about a red (bell) pepper or a cucumber. That shiny skin on the outside is due to the high levels of silica present.

Silica is known to activate certain enzymes that are involved in the production of collagen. While the turnover of collagen is extremely slow, it is vital that we do all we can to ensure that the production of high quality collagen is carried out as best as is physically possible for our body.

Best Food Sources – cucumbers, (bell) peppers, leeks, green beans.

Sulphur

Organic sulphur is one of the most important nutrients to the long-term beauty, structure and ageing of the skin. It is the most broadly used mineral in both the production and maintenance of the extracellular matrix – the lattice-like mesh that helps give tissues structural support. The main component of this matrix is a group of substances called proteoglycans. These are fibres that bind to collagen within the matrix to form this vast web of supportive material. Ensuring an adequate sulphur intake can have rather dramatic effects upon the appearance of the skin.

Best Food Sources – onions, garlic, leeks, eggs, fish.

Zinc

Zinc is one of the single most important nutrients for skin health. Male and female, young and old, will all benefit from an adequate intake of this nutrient.

The first major benefit from zinc is the fact that it is involved in the production and regulation of over 200 hormones, including the more powerful ones such as testosterone. Testosterone is the main hormone involved in instigating acne lesions. Testosterone, when converted into the aggressive form (dihydrotestosterone) can have a stimulatory effect upon the sebaceous glands. It causes them to start producing larger than necessary amounts of sebum. It also causes the sebum to become slightly thicker and more viscous. This high amount of thicker sebum creates an environment more conducive to the formation of comedones (blackheads). These are formed when sebum blocks a hair follicle and binds with keratin to make a thick sticky plug that bungs up the follicle. This sticky plug works like fly paper, trapping bacteria that normally live happily on the surface of the skin. These staphylococcus bacteria begin to accumulate in the sebum/keratin plug, and are able to instigate infection. There is then an active infection within the hair follicle, and an acne spot is born. By increasing our intake of zinc, the behaviour of testosterone can be kept in check and its effect upon sebaceous glands is far less aggressive.

Another added benefit of zinc is that it has another regulatory effect upon sebaceous glands, separate from that of hormonal control. It has the ability to help to regulate how the sebaceous glands are behaving. If the skin is too oily, zinc seems to have the ability to calm down sebaceous secretions. On the same note, if the skin is very dry, zinc seems to be able to increase sebaceous activity to normalize the oil content of the skin.

Best Food Sources – shellfish, pumpkin seeds, mushrooms, spinach.

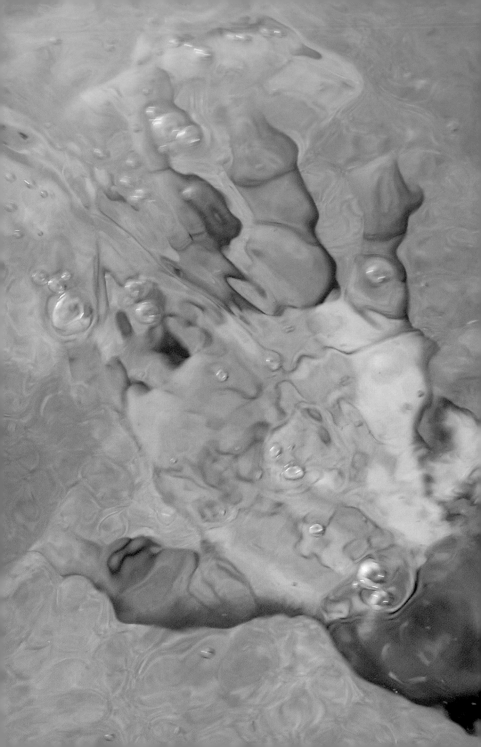

6

Antioxidants

Unless you have been inhabiting a different planet for the last 15 years, you will have heard of antioxidants. These seemingly mysterious compounds have become a real fashionable buzz word, and it is almost impossible to pick up a glossy magazine and turn the pages without at least seeing one reference to them. I think it is also fair to say that there is a great deal of hype surrounding antioxidants, and never have such nutrients been more misunderstood.

What is an Antioxidant?

In our bodies there is a constant battle taking place. Every cell in the body has the ability to create its own energy supply – a molecule called ATP – by metabolizing glucose from the food we eat. This is what keeps every cell alive, and is referred to as cellular respiration. During this process, a series of mischievous compounds, known as "free radicals", is formed. Now, I know that their name makes them sound like some extreme guerilla military group, but they are in fact a metabolic by-product that is chemically unbalanced.

Without getting too geeky, different chemicals and elements require a certain amount of electrons to be present within their outer structure in order to be "stable". If they don't have sufficient electrons in their outer orbit, they will desperately seek a spare electron. They generally do this by smashing into cells, trying to steal one from an unsuspecting cell. When this occurs the free radicals can cause a certain degree of damage to the genetic material within the cell, which can then lead to the cell functioning poorly, or even affect the way in which the cell behaves when it divides. In the light of this, there is a huge link between free radicals and the onset of cancers, and certainly the ageing of body tissues.

But, it's not all doom and gloom. The body actually produces its own free radical compounds that are of benefit to us in certain situations. The immune system is a prime example of this. Certain types of white blood cells within our immune system can secrete types of free radicals in order to assist in the inflammatory response when the body is coming under attack from an infectious agent or has been injured. However, not allowing these natural free radicals to get out of control can be a valuable key to symptomatic management of many different conditions and ailments.

Free radicals can also be formed when our body has to metabolize toxic compounds, such as those that enter our body from smoking, drinking too much alcohol, environmental pollutants and certain nasty dietary compounds. The free radicals produced from such environmental influences are far more abundant and aggressive than those formed by normal cellular respiration. That is why these influences are so closely associated with premature ageing.

Antioxidants are a natural solution to the electron problem faced by free radical compounds. By their very nature, antioxidants are essentially electron donors. They can donate an electron to the panicking free radical, thus disarming it and stopping it from causing trouble by damaging other cells in its quest for stability. However, it is a logical conclusion that once an antioxidant has donated an electron to a free radical, it itself then becomes a free radical.

Nature is a wonderful thing. When we consume foods that are naturally rich in antioxidants, they are also accompanied by a whole host of other active phytochemicals that help to recycle the antioxidants once they have donated their electron, and often you will find that antioxidant-rich foods contain several types of antioxidant, each with the ability to recycle one another.

A word of warning on this note: while it can be very useful to supplement with antioxidant nutrients to support many aspects of our health, it is always wise to look for a product that contains a whole range of different antioxidants. This way you can ensure that there are sufficient supportive compounds present to ensure adequate recycling, once the antioxidant has donated its electron. There is now a large amount of evidence to support negative effects arising from taking high doses of individual antioxidant nutrients in isolation – such as taking large doses of, let's say, beta carotene. This is because, without all the other supportive antioxidants and compounds to recycle it, taking individual antioxidants can in fact increase our free radical load and create more problems.

The Solubility Issue

If like me, you have tried virtually every single skincare brand on the market, you will have noticed that many products these days have different "added antioxidants" and extracts that are included to increase the antioxidant profile of the product. You may also be aware of many of the nutritional supplements aimed at skincare that seem to list endless antioxidants. This all sounds wonderful, but the unfortunate thing is that all antioxidants seem to have been bunched together, and that many people assume that they all do exactly the same thing. There are literally hundreds of compounds in the plant kingdom that can work as antioxidants in the body. It really stands to reason that the behaviour of these compounds will be as diverse as the array of antioxidants themselves. It is rather odd to assume that all antioxidants will do the same thing, be active in the same parts of the body, and be distributed in the body in similar ways.

In general terms, antioxidants can be split into two main groups: water-soluble antioxidants and fat-soluble antioxidants.

Water-soluble Antioxidants

Water-soluble antioxidants, as the name suggests, are water-soluble compounds. This means that they can happily be absorbed through the gut wall but will then mainly deliver their benefits within the systemic circulation. They, therefore, will offer great protection to the lining of blood vessels, as well as to some areas of the liver and kidneys, etc. These compounds don't stay in the body very long, and are rapidly excreted via the kidneys. Water-soluble antioxidants include vitamin C.

Fat-soluble Antioxidants

Fat-soluble antioxidants, on the other hand, will behave slightly differently. By their very nature, they will not stay in systemic circulation for long. This is because they will naturally seek a fat-rich environment. They will rapidly migrate into fatty tissues, such as the eyes and, of course, the fatty subcutaneous layer of the skin. When they move into these tissues, they generally stay there until they are fully spent and broken down, as there is seldom any kind of physiological mechanism present that can pull them out of fatty tissues back into circulation. As such, they are present for much longer and can begin to accumulate, and deliver their effects for a much longer period of time. Fat-soluble antioxidants include beta carotene.

It is the fat-soluble antioxidants that are of greatest interest in the context of skin health. These compounds will naturally begin to migrate into the fatty subcutaneous layer of the skin. It is in this layer of the skin that the collagen matrix, the lattice-like structure that gives skin its structural support, has its roots. This collagen matrix can frequently come under free radical attack from a whole host of different environmental influences. Therefore we need to supply adequate antioxidant protection in order to reduce the extent of any damage that may occur. Damage to the collagen matrix can cause wrinkles, and cause the skin to sag and lose elasticity (just think of the wrinkled mouth of a long term smoker) Fat-soluble antioxidants, such as the carotenoids (beta carotene, alpha carotene, astaxanthin, etc) can offer this protection. When they move into the subcutaneous layer, they quickly accumulate and can lie in waiting for any opportunistic free radicals, ready to disarm them before they can cause any damage. To ensure that we have adequate levels of fat-soluble antioxidants present at all times to offer such protection, it is vital that every day we consume foods that are naturally rich in them.

It is worth mentioning here that we also need to ensure that we consume these foods with a good quality fat source. This simple combination will ensure that the fat-soluble antioxidants get taken up much more effectively in the digestive tract. This can be as simple as creating a tomato and red (bell) pepper salad, with an olive oil based dressing. The tomatoes and (bell) peppers are dense sources of fat-soluble carotenoids. The addition of the olive oil dressing drastically increases the solubility of these compounds, and gives an ideal transport vehicle to carry these wonderful antioxidants across the gut wall.

It also stands to reason that we should generally follow a diet and lifestyle that minimizes the production of free radicals in the body. It is impossible to avoid them completely, as their formation is a normal part of metabolic activity. However, certain foods and lifestyle choices can cause a huge surge in free radical production. Smoking is a perfect example of this. Excessive alcohol intake and consuming too much fried food and overly processed food also causes a massive increase in free radical production. So, you guessed it, the usual healthy lifestyle message is key to long-term skin health. Don't smoke, keep the booze to a minimum, and consume a diet that is predominantly fresh, wholefood-based and rich in the types of food outlined in this book.

7
Face Fats

In modern times we seem to have become completely obsessed with fat. Low fat this, reduced fat that. It has become a demonized nutrient. In some cases, it is certainly wise to reduce our fat intake. Saturated animal fats, such as those found in red meat, can trigger inflammatory issues in the body, which can be damaging to the heart, the circulatory system and the joints, and can even worsen some skin lesions like eczema and psoriasis. However, the trend that most health-conscious people take is to go "low fat" on almost everything, and this can be detrimental to many aspects of our health.

Fats are a vital nutrient for our body. Virtually every single hormone in the body is manufactured from fat. This includes oestrogen, testosterone, etc. Fats are also the key structural materials used for the creation of different communication molecules, and structural components necessary for normal day-to-day functioning of the body. They also provide the source material for the manufacture of nutrients. So, as you can imagine, cutting them out completely can be bad for long-term health.

The key is to make sure that you choose the right types of fat, not guzzling down pizza and chips every night. The emphasis should be upon unsaturated fats such as those found in nuts and seeds, oily fish, avocados, olives, etc. These fats are the ones that our body needs every day for correct functioning.

Omega 3 Fatty Acids

Unless you have been living in a cave, or have distanced yourself from all forms of communication in the last decade, chances are you have heard a lot about omega 3 and the myriad benefits that it delivers. Most commonly found in oily fish, and some seeds such as flax and hemp, omega 3 is a vital yet widely deficient nutrient.

Anti-inflammatory Action

Omega 3 fatty acids are one of the most important tools that we have at our disposal for the treatment of any type of inflammatory issue. When we process and metabolize dietary fats, one of the major metabolic end products is a group of communication molecules known as prostaglandins. One of the main roles of the prostaglandins is to regulate different aspects of the inflammatory response.

There are three different types of prostaglandin: series 1, series 2 and series 3. Series 1 and series 3 are involved in dampening down and deactivating the inflammatory response. Series 2 prostaglandins, in contrast, are involved in the instigation of the inflammatory response, and can make any currently active inflammation worse.

The type of prostaglandins produced will depend on the type of dietary fat that is consumed. Saturated animal fats, for example, are very high in a fatty acid called arachidonic acid, which when metabolized, causes a rise in series 2 prostaglandins – the ones responsible for exacerbating inflammation. A diet high in omega 3 fatty acids, however, will cause an increase in the production of series 1 and series 3 prostaglandins – the ones that tackle inflammation. So, in essence, manipulating our dietary fat intake can directly influence the inflammatory response in our body. Remember that virtually all skin lesions involve inflammation. The red itchy flare-ups of eczema, the painful swelling of acne, are all signs of active inflammation. So, any techniques we can adopt to make this less severe are of huge importance.

Cell Membrane Health

Every cell in our body has a fatty membrane that gives the cell its shape, keeps the cell contents in, and toxins and pathogens out. Cell membranes are made of a double layer of a fatty substance called phospholipids. The cell membranes also house a whole array of different receptors and transporters. These complex and highly organized structures allow interactions between the inner workings of the cell and its outer environment. They allow hormones to bind to the cell and instigate changes to the way in which the cell behaves. They allow nutrients to successfully enter the cell, and for waste material to be ejected. A healthy membrane means a healthy cell, which means healthy tissues.

Cell membranes require a constant stream of fatty acids in order to be able to constantly maintain themselves, to ensure that they remain soft, supple and strong, and that their many receptor sites, etc, remain fully functional. As you have probably guessed by now, the fats required for this maintenance are the omega 3 fatty acids.

If the membranes of skin cells are working optimally, the skin as an organ will function much better. There will be better oxygen delivery, better transport of nutrients to the area, and also the skin's ability to retain moisture will be greatly improved. There is another added plus point. As the skin starts to behave better as an organ, the effects of any topical products that we use on our skin, such as moisturisers, face masks, etc, will be greatly enhanced.

Omega 6 Fatty Acids

The other most widely known fatty acid is the omega 6 fatty acid. This is found in the highest concentrations in seed oils.

Hanging in the Balance

Omega 6 fatty acids have some vitally important functions in the body. When converted in the right way, they can also deliver some anti-inflammatory effects, which have been well documented in cases of eczema and acne.

However, there are issues surrounding omega 6 fatty acids, mainly around the way in which they convert during their metabolism. Omega 6 can, when consumed in levels beyond daily requirements, be converted into series 2 prostaglandins – the ones that activate and exacerbate inflammation. They can also be converted into another inflammatory stimulator – lipoxygenase. In addition, there is new evidence emerging that some by-products of omega 6 fatty acids are found in all acne lesions, and are believed to be part of the instigation process of this condition.

Balancing Act

The key to ensuring that essential fatty acids deliver the benefits described above is ensuring we have the right balance of them in our diet. We need a ratio of 2:1, in favour of omega 3. That's twice as much omega 3 than omega 6. However, for many in the Western world, this ratio is completely reversed. This has led to devastating patterns of disease. There are now links between excessive omega 6 fatty acid consumption and serious diseases such as cardiovascular disease, inflammatory conditions such as arthritis, and some types of cancer. In relation to skin health, this can trigger or exacerbate inflammatory lesions such as eczema. So, it is vital that we get this ratio right.

This balancing act can often lead to quite a bit of head scratching and guesswork, so what I recommend is that people focus upon getting extra omega 3 into their diet, and don't worry about consuming any extra omega 6, as generally we tend to get more than enough from the usual array of foods that seem to dominate our diets in this part of the world. This means you should eat plenty of oily fish such as salmon, mackerel, sardines and anchovies. You can also get some omega 3 fatty acids from plant sources, such as flax seeds, and even some types of algae. There are also some great ready mixed omega 3 oils on the market that you can just add to recipes, as I've done in the Hemp Seed and Artichoke Stuffed (Bell) Pepper recipe on page 132.

8
Soups

Mean Green Mineralizing Machine

Serves 2-4

This soup is highly potent! It is very green, very strongly flavoured and is also virtually 100 per cent raw! It is a powerful source of minerals, which will do wonders for your skin.

2 cloves of garlic, finely chopped
1 white onion, finely chopped
2 large cucumbers, diced
1 large yellow (bell) pepper, halved, stalk and seeds removed
1 ripe avocado, halved, stone removed
2 handfuls of baby spinach
3 tablespoons curly parsley, coarsely chopped
1 tablespoon fresh coriander, coarsely chopped
1 tablespoon fresh basil, coarsely chopped
400 ml/14 fl oz/1½ cups approx of extra virgin olive oil

1. Add a little olive oil to a pan, along with the garlic and the onion, and a good pinch of sea salt. Sauté until the onion has softened.
2. Place all the remaining ingredients in a food processor.
3. Add the sautéed onion and garlic to the food processor.
4. Blend into a thick, vivid green soup.

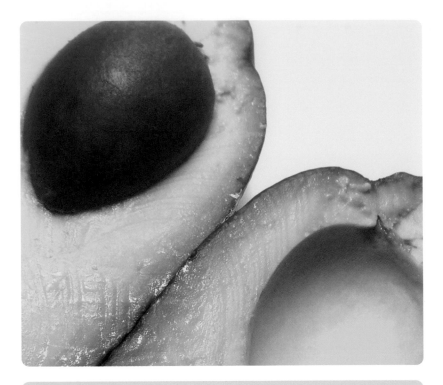

Benefits

Cucumbers

Cucumbers may seem to serve very little nutritional purpose, but they are actually very rich in one of the most important minerals for skin health: silica. This is the mineral that gives cucumbers the thick shiny coating on their skin. Silica helps to support the structure and function of the extracellular matrix, and also supports collagen.

Yellow (Bell) Peppers

All (bell) peppers are antioxidant-rich. Yellow (bell) peppers are very high in a flavonoid compound called lutein which is responsible for their vivid yellow colour. Lutein helps protect the fatty membranes of our cells from free radical damage.

Avocados

I hear time and time again people avoiding these super nutritious gifts from nature because they have a high fat content. I hope from reading the Face Fats chapter that you now realize how important the right types of fat are for the health and appearance of your skin. Avocados are incredibly rich in essential fatty acids that plump up and smooth out the skin. They are also a wonderful source of vitamin E, which helps to protect our skin cells from free radical damage. Vitamin E has a particular affinity for free radicals derived from damaged fats.

Spinach

Spinach is a very rich source of the plant form of vitamin A: beta carotene. It's another potent antioxidant. There are reasonable levels of vitamin C present too. Spinach is also a great source of magnesium, selenium, and some zinc to boot!

Parsley

Parsley is dense in so many nutrients. It is one of the richest sources of vitamin C in existence, gram for gram. It is also high in essential oils, some of which are renowned as natural diuretic agents. This helps increase urinary output and increase the kidneys' removal of water-soluble waste products. There is also a flavonoid compound found in parsley called luteolin, which is another potent antioxidant.

Extra Virgin Olive Oil

Extra virgin olive oil has had a reputation as a beauty food around the Mediterranean for decades. This is partially due to the high content of beneficial fats such as omega 9, and much focus has been placed upon this. However, much of its benefit is derived from the presence of a group of powerful antioxidant compounds known as polyphenols. These are similar to the antioxidants in green tea, and are many times more powerful than the more well known antioxidants such as vitamin E, etc. They help protect the fatty membranes of our cells from biochemical warfare by free radicals.

Tomato and Fennel Soup

Serves 2-4

I have to admit I don't make my own vegetable stock but just use a good quality vegetable bouillon. I generally make up a litre/2 pints and add whatever is needed to the recipe, storing any leftover in the fridge for the next day or in the freezer for later use.

2 tablespoons extra virgin olive oil
1 large red onion, finely chopped
2 cloves of garlic, finely chopped
1 small fennel bulb, finely chopped
1 teaspoon crushed fennel seed
2 x 400 g/14 oz cans of chopped tomatoes
3 tablespoons orange juice
vegetable stock
½ teaspoon apple cider vinegar
freshly ground black pepper

1. Add the olive oil, chopped onion, chopped garlic and chopped fennel, along with a generous pinch of sea salt to a saucepan, and sauté until the onion and fennel have softened.
2. Add the fennel seed, tomatoes and orange juice. Then add enough stock to just cover.
3. Simmer for 10 minutes.
4. Use a hand blender to blend into a smooth vibrant soup.

Benefits

Onions and Garlic
Onions and garlic, like all members of the allium family, are very rich in sulphur, which is vital for the structure of the skin. Sulphur is a key constituent in the extracellular matrix, the net-like structure that, along with collagen, gives the skin sturdiness.

Fennel
Fennel is well known as a digestive aid, but of interest here is its activity as a diuretic. It has the ability to increase urinary output, thus aiding the kidneys in the removal of water-soluble waste products. Keeping the body clean from within is a top priority in the quest for clear, glowing skin.

Tomatoes
Tomatoes are bursting with some powerful antioxidant compounds. They are high in beta carotene, lycopene and a whole host of active flavonoids, all delivering protection against free radical damage.

Beetroot (Beet) and Horseradish Soup

Serves 1–2

This bright purple powerhouse will get you tingling all over and glowing from within.

1 red onion, finely sliced
1 large potato, diced
1 bunch of small/medium beetroot (beet), washed and diced, leaves discarded
vegetable stock (see page 100)
3 tablespoons horseradish sauce

1. Add a little olive oil to a pan, along with the sliced red onion, and a good pinch of sea salt.
2. Sauté the onion until it has softened.
3. Add the potato and beetroot (beet), cover with stock and simmer until the vegetables soften.
4. Add the horseradish sauce, then blend to make a thick velvety soup.

Benefits

Beetroot (Beet)
This contains some very interesting and powerful chemistry. There is a group of chemicals called betalains, one of which, betacyanin, is responsible for the deep purple colour of beetroot (beet) – which reminds me, don't eat this soup if you are wearing white. Betalains are known for their influence upon liver function. They increase the activity of certain detoxification processes, involved in breaking down bodily wastes, and carrying them away for removal via the bowel. This is mainly via the glutathione enzymatic system. Beetroot (beet) is also very rich in the powerful antioxidant compound zeaxanthin, which protects the fatty subcutaneous tissue from damage. Free radical mediated damage to this tissue can have significant impact upon the skin becoming saggy and dull.

Proper (Bell) Pepper Soup

Serves 2-4

This soup is gorgeous and nutrient-rich. Serve with a nice lump of fresh wholemeal bread, and get transported to heaven!

1 red onion, coarsely chopped
2 cloves of garlic, finely chopped
3 red (bell) peppers, coarsely chopped
1 large sweet potato, diced
vegetable stock (see page 100)

1. Sauté the onion and garlic along with a pinch of salt in a little olive oil, until the onion has softened.
2. Add the red (bell) peppers and sweet potato to the pan with the onion and garlic.
3. Add enough vegetable stock to cover all the ingredients, and simmer until the potatoes have softened.
4. At this point, use a hand blender, or add to a food processor, and blend into a smooth soup.

Benefits

Red (Bell) Peppers

Red (bell) peppers are bursting with a whole range of powerful compounds. The chemicals responsible for the deep vivid red colour are compounds called flavonoids, which have a very powerful antioxidant property. All varieties of (bell) pepper contain a large amount of a compound called beta carotene, which is also a colour pigment, ranging from yellow to deep orange. Beta carotene is the plant source of vitamin A. Beta carotene is also a fat-soluble antioxidant. This means that it will be most active within fatty tissues, especially the fatty areas of subcutaneous tissue of the skin. This will help to protect the skin from free radical damage, and can help to maintain elasticity and plumpness.

Helpful Hint: When buying red (bell) peppers, buy the darkest coloured ones that you can find. The darker they are, the higher the concentration of the antioxidant flavonoids.

Sweet Potatoes

Sweet potatoes are also very rich sources of beta carotene. It is this compound that is responsible for the vivid orange colour of their flesh.

Spiced Parsnip Soup

Serves 2-4

This delectable soup is a digestive dynamo. The better your digestion, the better your skin!

1 large white onion, coarsely chopped
1 clove of garlic, finely chopped
2.5 cm/1 inch piece of ginger, peeled and finely chopped
½ teaspoon cinnamon powder
½ teaspoon mild curry powder
6 parsnips, cut into chunks
vegetable stock (see page 100)

1. Sauté the onion and garlic, along with the spices and a pinch of salt, in a little olive oil, until the onion softens.
2. Add the chopped parsnips and enough stock to cover all the ingredients. Simmer until the parsnips are soft.
3. Blend into a smooth soup.

Benefits

Parsnips
Parsnips are very rich in a special kind of sugar called fructo oligo saccharide (FOS), which is a very potent prebiotic. Prebiotics stimulate the growth of good bacteria in the digestive tract. These good bacteria help to regulate almost every aspect of digestion and absorption to varying degrees. Good digestive housekeeping is vital for clear radiant skin. If we allow our digestive functions to become sluggish and ineffective, we run the risk of auto-toxicity. This is a state where waste products begin to "over ferment" in the digestive tract, leaving behind some rather undesirable waste products, which can then be absorbed into systemic circulation. Auto toxicity has been linked with many skin conditions, including eczema, psoriasis and acne.

Ginger
Ginger is a wonderful natural anti-inflammatory compound. Many skin lesions (eczema and psoriasis flare-ups, acne, etc) involve a localized inflammatory response. It is this that causes the redness usually seen in such conditions. The essential oils that give ginger its distinctive spicy aroma and flavour are responsible for its anti-inflammatory activity. They reduce the activity of an enzyme called Cyclo-Oxygenase 2 (COX-2), which is involved in triggering the inflammatory response.

Spicy Black Bean and Jerusalem Artichoke Soup

Serves 2–4

This is quite a filling soup, and a great digestive tonic to boot!

1 red onion, finely chopped
2 cloves of garlic, finely chopped
1 stick of celery, finely chopped
3 Jerusalem artichokes, diced
400 g/14 oz can of black beans, drained
vegetable stock (see page 100)

1. Add the onion, garlic and celery to a pan with a little olive oil, and sauté until the onion softens.
2. At this point, add the Jerusalem artichokes and the black beans, and add enough vegetable stock to just cover the ingredients.
3. Simmer until the Jerusalem artichokes soften.
4. Blend until smooth.

Benefits

Black Beans
Black beans are definitely the unsung heroes in the world of pulses. They are bursting to the hilt with nutrients and phytochemicals. Firstly, they are rich sources of the B vitamins, which help to support almost every aspect of skin physiology. Secondly, they are rich in zinc, which helps regulate oil production in the skin, and they also support immunity which can help in managing infected skin lesions.

However, black beans really come into their own when we look at their phytochemistry. The black pigment on their outer layer is made up of a complex of different anthocyanins. These are the same colour pigments that are found in red grapes, blueberries, acai berries, etc. They include compounds such as delphinidin, petunidin and malvidin. These compounds deliver some notable anti-inflammatory activity so can be a useful part of managing any inflammatory skin lesion.

Black beans also have a very high level of non-soluble fibre. This is true of all beans and pulses, but the insoluble fibre in black beans is rather unique. This is because gut bacteria can easily ferment it down to create a substance called butyric acid. This magic compound has an almost rejuvenative effect on the gut wall, so can massively enhance elimination, plus the absorption of some nutrients. These two things combined will help to improve overall nutritional status, which can only aid the skin in functioning better as an organ.

Jerusalem Artichokes
These wonderful and unusual vegetables are another digestive dynamo. They contain special types of sugar called fructo oligosaccharides and inulin that work as a food source for the good bacteria in the gut. When gut flora feed on these vital sugars, they start to reproduce, further enhancing the strength of the good gut flora. This will then improve elimination and nutrient absorption.

9
Starters

Roasted Beetroot (Beet) with Horseradish and Rocket (Arugula) Salad

Serves 2-4

Beetroot (beet) are packed with so many skin-healthy nutrients. The unlikely marriage of beetroot (beet) and horseradish is a match made in heaven.

3 small raw beetroot (beet)
Extra virgin olive oil
1 tablespoon horseradish sauce
Fresh rocket (arugula)

1. Preheat the oven to 220°C/425°F/Gas Mark 7. Scrub the beetroot (beet), but leave the skins on. Cut into cubes, and place into a roasting tin. Drizzle with the olive oil and some sea salt. Place into the hot oven, and roast until the beetroot (beet) is soft, and the skin has become crispy.
2. Place the roasted beetroot (beet) into a bowl and stir through a generous dollop of horseradish sauce. Serve over a bed of fresh rocket (arugula).

Benefits

Beetroot (Beet)

This is a rich source of many potent antioxidant compounds, but most exciting of all is that it contains a compound called betacyanin – the deep purple pigment that stains anything it comes into contact with. Betacyanin is a fabulous skin tonic, for the simple reason that it helps to give the liver a bit of a kick start. It is known to stimulate a group of chemical reactions called the cytochrome P450 enzyme pathway in the liver that helps in biotransformation of waste products. The quicker we deal with our natural waste products, the better when it comes to healthy happy skin.

Rocket (Arugula)
Rocket (arugula) is a wonderful ingredient that can have very beneficial effects upon the way in which the body deals with and processes fats. It contains a very powerful group of bitter-tasting chemicals. When specific taste buds on the tongue detect this bitter taste, a sudden nervous reflex takes place. There are two major nerves that supply this region of the tongue. These are the vagus and the hypoglossal nerves. When the taste buds detect the bitter flavour, there is a sudden potent stimulation of these two nerves. These nerves supply the upper digestive tract and the liver so when they are stimulated in such a way they cause the liver to start producing more bile and, at the same time, cause the gall bladder to contract, releasing bile into the upper part of the intestine.

Bile is one of the key factors in the digestion and absorption of dietary fats, including those all important good fats that we need for vibrant skin health. The bile salts, when released from the gall bladder, will mix with fats in the digestive tract and emulsify them, turning them into small droplets called micelles that are then ready to be easily absorbed through the gut wall. It is vital that we are able to absorb fats effectively, especially if we are making the effort to increase our intake of those all important good fats. Consuming bitter tasting foods can certainly go a long way to helping us absorb fats properly.

Roasted Red (Bell) Pepper and Cannellini Dip

Serves 2-4

This is an amazing starter when served in a small ramekin with corn chips, and a few vegetable crudités.

2 red (bell) peppers, sliced lengthways
1 x 400 g/14 oz can of cannellini beans, drained
1 clove of garlic, finely chopped
4 tablespoons extra virgin olive oil

1. Preheat the oven to 220°C/425°F/Gas Mark 7. Add the sliced (bell) peppers to a roasting tin, and drizzle a little olive oil over them. Place into the hot oven, and roast until the (bell) peppers are soft and start to get a little charred on the outside. At this point they are done.

2. Add the roasted (bell) peppers, beans, garlic and oil to a food processor, along with a little crystal salt. Blend into a thick, smooth dip.

Benefits

Cannellini Beans

Cannellini beans are one of my favourite ingredients. They are a wonderful source of dietary fibre. This is very important for maintaining digestive health and ensuring full and rapid removal of waste products, avoiding auto toxicity.

Cannellini beans are a good source of zinc, which can prove to be a vital nutrient in managing acne. Zinc has the ability to regulate the function of the sebaceous glands that secrete oil into the skin. If they are over active, zinc seems to be able to calm them down and even out oil production, which can reduce breakouts. Zinc also regulates testosterone production and activity, which can often be out of balance in many cases of acne.

Red (Bell) Peppers

The rich red colour of red (bell) peppers is due to the high concentration of antioxidant flavonoids, which can help protect the skin from free radical damage. There is direct correlation between the intake of foods high in antioxidants over a lifetime, and the overall ageing of the skin.

Crostini with Olive and Artichoke Pâté

Serves 2–4

This is a flavour explosion and fabulous for the health of the skin.

1 x 200 g/7 oz can of artichoke hearts
4 tablespoons chopped green olives
3 tablespoons olive oil
Good quality ciabatta bread, sliced

1. Simply add the artichokes, olives and olive oil to a food processor and blend into a smooth pâté.
2. Spread this luscious pâté on slices of toasted ciabatta, and enjoy as a crostini.

Benefits

Artichokes

Artichokes are a rich source of caffeoylquinic acid, which is known to increase both the production of bile and also the rate at which it is released from the gall bladder. Bile is one of the major transport mechanisms for fat-soluble toxins. Increasing their rate of removal can help to keep the skin clear. Bile is also vitally important in the correct digestion and utilization of dietary fats. Increasing the absorption of good fats can give the skin a plump dewy texture and increase its ability to hold onto moisture. Good all round.

Olives

Olives have long been associated with beauty and skin health. They are a very rich source of the antioxidant nutrient vitamin E. Vitamin E helps to reduce free radical damage within fatty tissues and cell membranes, so may be a vital nutrient for reducing skin ageing and improving overall skin appearance.

Smoked Salmon with Asparagus and Chilli Lime Dressing

Serves 1

This very simple salad is light but packed with skin-saving nutrients.

5–6 pieces of asparagus
3 slices of good quality smoked salmon

For the Dressing
Juice of ½ lime
½ red chilli, deseeded and finely chopped
1 teaspoon honey
1 tablespoon soy sauce
2 teaspoons toasted sesame oil

1. In a small container, combine all of the dressing ingredients. Mix well and leave aside.
2. Immerse the asparagus into a pan of boiling water for no longer than 2 minutes, just long enough for it to turn bright green and soften slightly.
3. Lay the asparagus onto the serving plate side by side, and lay the slices of smoked salmon on top. Cover with the dressing and serve.

Benefits

Smoked Salmon

Salmon is a massively dense source of the all-important omega 3 fatty acids. These fats deliver many benefits to the skin. They help to maintain the structure of skin cells, enabling the cells to function more efficiently, and therefore help the skin tissue to remain healthy. By making skin cells healthier, omega 3 fatty acids also help the skin to retain moisture more effectively, thus helping to give smoother skin. However, what I personally think is the most important function of omega 3 fatty acids is their influence upon the inflammatory response.

Many skin conditions feature an inflammatory element, which displays itself as redness (think acne and eczema), which is one of the worst aspects of these lesions. There are a series of communication chemicals in the body known as prostaglandins, which are involved in regulating the inflammatory response. Some activate inflammation and worsen pain, whereas others switch inflammation off and reduce pain. These compounds are made directly from dietary fats that we consume.

Saturated animal fats and too much omega 6 fat cause the body to manufacture the prostaglandins that switch on and worsen inflammation. Omega 3 fatty acids, however, cause the body to manufacture the types of prostaglandins that switch off inflammation.

So, by manipulating our dietary fat intake, we can directly manipulate the inflammatory response.

Spinach Pâté on Toasted Soda Bread

Serves 1–2

This is just total comfort food, or as a single portion makes an amazing starter. Soda bread is a lot easier on the digestive system for most people than bread made using yeast.

1 clove of garlic
25 g/1 oz butter
225 g/8 oz cooked (steamed) spinach, finely chopped
150 g/5 oz low-fat cream cheese
½ teaspoon nutmeg
soda bread

1. Sauté the garlic in the butter for about 2–3 minutes, until the garlic has become fragrant.
2. Place all the other ingredients except the soda bread into a mixing bowl. Add the garlic and mix well.
3. Place into a smaller bowl or container, and refrigerate for 3–4 hours.
4. Serve on a sliver of toasted soda bread.

Benefits

Spinach

Spinach is packed with a whole host of nutrients, but the one that is of most benefit to the skin is the fat-soluble antioxidant beta carotene. This antioxidant compound will move into the subcutis layer of the skin and protect from free radical damage that dense array of structural fibres there.

10
Main Courses

Moroccan Style Veggie Tagine

Serves 2-4

2 cloves of garlic, finely chopped
1 large red onion, finely chopped
coconut oil
1 medium courgette, sliced
1 large handful of dates
1 x 400 g/14 oz can of chopped tomatoes
200 g/7 oz cooked chickpeas
1½ teaspoons cinnamon powder

1. Sauté the garlic and onion in a little coconut oil, with a pinch of salt, until the onion has softened.
2. Add the courgette and dates, and continue to sauté until the courgette begins to soften.
3. At this point, add the chopped tomatoes, chickpeas and cinnamon. Simmer until the sauce becomes a fragrant, sweet, thick delight.
4. Serve with couscous or quinoa, and a good side salad.

Benefits

Onions and Garlic

Onions and garlic, like all the alliums, are rich in organic sulphur. This essential mineral is vital for skin health. It is a key constituent in the protein matrix that supports the skin's structural integrity. It also assists in normal cellular detoxification pathways, helping tissue to break down and remove waste materials. This in itself can give the skin an extra glow.

Tomatoes

Tomatoes are a very rich source of a potent antioxidant compound called lycopene. Most commonly associated with prostate health, lycopene is actually a great antioxidant for the skin. This is because it is a member of the lipid soluble carotenoid group of compounds. These substances can begin to accumulate in the subcutaneous tissue where they help to protect the collagen matrix present there from free radical attack, maintaining elasticity and strength.

Chickpeas

Chickpeas are a good source of the mineral zinc. This vital metal is of prime importance in skin health. It is used by the sebaceous glands to regulate sebum production. If skin is too oily, adequate zinc can help to reduce sebaceous secretions. If the skin is a little dry, adequate zinc intake can increase skin lubrication. Chickpeas are also a great source of fibre, thus working as an internal housekeeper for the digestive tract. Fibre helps to keep the bowel moving, and as such helps to remove waste materials from the body. Keeping the digestive system moving is the key to glowing vibrant skin, as even a slight accumulation of waste in the gastrointestinal tract can lead to "auto toxicity" – essentially reabsorption of our own waste products, which will make the skin look dull and tired, not to mention leaving you feeling far from healthy.

Coconut Oil

As well as being a heart-healthy cooking oil option, coconut oil in this dish works as a potentiator. To really drive home the carotenoids, such as the lycopene in the tomatoes, it is ideal if we can consume them with a high quality fat source. As they are fat-soluble nutrients, when they are ingested with a high quality, easily absorbed fat source, they are much more rapidly and fully absorbed and send happily on their way to fatty tissues, than if they were consumed in isolation. They literally form a complex with the fat and are carried across the gut wall with droplets of fat.

Steamed Salmon with Yogurt Sauce on Wilted Greens

Serves 1

This recipe is divine and incredibly nutrient dense, yet is an ideal choice for those evenings when you just fancy something light.

1 salmon fillet
1 handful of shredded spring greens (collard greens)
1 clove of garlic, finely chopped
2 spring onions, finely chopped
1 small pot of fat-free yogurt
1 handful of fresh dill, finely chopped

For the Salmon
Place the salmon into a steamer tray, and steam for 15–20 minutes. It is a very fast cooking fish so this should be more than enough.

For the Greens
Add them to the steamer after the salmon has been steaming for about 10–12 minutes. Remove them at the same time as you remove the salmon.

For the Sauce
Prepare the sauce last, just before the dish is ready to serve. Sauté the garlic and the spring onions in a little olive oil, until they both soften slightly. Transfer the yogurt into a small bowl. Add the sautéed garlic and spring onion to the yogurt. Add the chopped dill and mix well.

To Assemble

Place the greens onto the centre of the plate, then place the salmon on top of them. Spoon the yogurt sauce over the salmon, ready to serve.

Benefits

Salmon

Salmon is high in the "skin saviour" omega 3 fatty acids. These fats help to maintain the structure and performance of cell membranes within the skin, allowing it to retain moisture more effectively. Omega 3 fatty acids also help to combat inflammatory issues, such as the redness associated with many common skin ailments.

Spring Greens (Collard Greens)

These are one of the most nutrient dense foods around. They are particularly rich in beta carotene, the fat-soluble antioxidant that can work wonders for long-term protection of collagen and elastin fibres.

Hemp Seed and Artichoke Stuffed (Bell) Peppers

Serves 1

This dish is amazing. It is light, yet it is a flavour explosion, and so nutrient dense that you don't feel as if you're missing out on anything after eating it. Who said light meals can't be satisfying?

4 tablespoons shelled hemp seeds
2 tablespoons marinated artichoke hearts
1 clove of garlic
2 tablespoons omega 3-6-9 oil
1 red (bell) pepper, halved and deseeded

1. Preheat the oven to 220°C/425°F/Gas Mark 7. Add a small amount of water to the bottom of a shallow roasting tin. Place in the hot oven.
2. Meanwhile, add the hemp seeds, artichoke hearts, garlic and omega oil, along with a generous pinch of sea salt, to a food processor, and blend into a coarse purée.
3. Remove the roasting tin from the oven. The water should be steaming hot. Place the (bell) pepper halves face down in the water, and return the tin to the oven, for about 10 minutes. After 10 minutes, check on the (bell) peppers. The skin should be just starting to blister. At this point, drain most of the water out of the roasting tin, leaving just a tiny bit behind in the bottom. Turn the (bell) peppers over, and fill them with the hemp and artichoke purée, and bake for a further 15 minutes. Remove from the oven and serve with some brown rice and salad.

Benefits

Red (Bell) Peppers

Red (bell) peppers are a very concentrated source of the skin-friendly antioxidant compounds carotenoids. These fat-soluble compounds, responsible for the deep red colour pigment, will naturally move into the subcutaneous layer of the skin, offering the base of the collagen matrix protection against free radical damage.

Artichokes

Artichokes are a fabulous skin food, for two distinct reasons. The compound caffeoylquinic acid increases both the production of bile in the liver, and the rate at which the liver releases this extra bile. This has a twofold effect. Increased bile levels mean a far greater digestion and absorption of dietary fats. If you are making efforts to increase your intake of essential fatty acids, then this effect on bile will enable you to absorb them more fully and efficiently. The second benefit of increased bile production and flow is that the liver gets a helping hand. When the liver processes the myriad of compounds that come its way each day, it transforms them into compounds that are less harmful and easier for the body to absorb. It does this by making these substances either water-soluble or fat-soluble. Water-soluble processed matter gets sent to the kidneys for removal via the urine. Fat-soluble compounds produced after biotransformation in the liver get sent to the bowel, via the bile, for removal with a bowel movement. If we increase the production and flow of bile, we give a much more effective transport system for such processed matter.

Hemp Seeds

Hemp seeds are a fantastic skin food. They are a rich source of the mineral zinc. Zinc is used by the sebaceous glands to regulate oil production. Skin that is too oily often evens out and normalizes with adequate zinc intake. Conversely, very dry skin often becomes more moist and soft with adequate zinc intake. The other major benefit of hemp seed is the essential fatty acid composition. It is a rich source of both omega 3 and omega 6 fatty acids, which can have a multitude of benefits on the skin, as previously mentioned. However, in this instance it is important to note that the cooking process will affect the EFA levels and composition slightly.

Sweet Potato and Spinach Curry

Serves 2-4

This is a quick and easy curry, ideal for a fast, healthy, nutrient-packed meal after a busy day.

2 cloves of garlic, finely chopped
1 red onion, finely chopped
coconut oil
2 tablespoons Madras or balti curry paste
400 g/14 oz can of coconut milk
2 medium sized sweet potatoes, diced
200 g/7 oz spinach

1. Fry the garlic and onion in a little coconut oil until soft. Stir in the paste and fry for 2 minutes.
2. Add the coconut milk and sweet potatoes and cook until just tender, about 10 minutes.
3. Stir through the spinach until wilted. Serve with brown rice, or quinoa.

Benefits

Sweet Potato
Sweet potatoes are a very rich source of that skin-loving antioxidant beta carotene. This compound moves into the subcutaneous layer of the skin, where it can deliver antioxidant support to the collagen and elastin matrix that has its roots here. Beta carotene can also deliver some anti-inflammatory activity, which can be useful in angry red skin conditions.

Spinach
Spinach is also a very dense source of beta carotene and other compounds in the carotenoid family.

Onions and Garlic
All of the allium family (onions, garlic, leeks, chives, etc) are very dense in organic sulphur. This vital mineral is involved in the manufacture of the extracellular matrix which, along with collagen, helps the skin keep its structural integrity.

Salmon and Tomato Skewers with Nutty Quinoa and a Spinach Salad

Serves 1

This is one of my favourite combinations of ingredients, not only for the flavours of the ingredients, but also for the way that I feel after eating it. It always leaves me feeling fantastic and energized.

1 large clove of garlic
Handful of basil leaves
1 tablespoon olive oil
1 large salmon fillet, cut into large cubes
3 cherry tomatoes
2 handfuls of quinoa
2 teaspoons vegetable stock powder
2 handfuls of baby spinach

1. Finely chop the garlic and basil together at the same time, working the two ingredients together to form a coarse paste.
2. Place the basil and garlic mixture into a small bowl, along with the olive oil, and mix thoroughly to create a marinade.
3. Add the cubed salmon to this mixture, and mix everything together well, ensuring the salmon is well coated in marinade.
4. Leave in the fridge to marinate for an hour.
5. After a suitable marinating time, remove the cubed salmon and add onto a skewer, along with the tomatoes. Alternate between salmon cube and tomato.

6. Place the quinoa grains into a saucepan, and cover with hot water and the vegetable stock powder and place on a high heat. Once at boiling point, leave to simmer for 20 minutes. When the quinoa has been simmering for 5 minutes, place the salmon skewers under a hot grill. Grill for 15 minutes, turning frequently.
7. Serve the salmon skewer over the cooked quinoa. Add the spinach and tomato side salad, tossed with your favourite dressing.

Benefits

Salmon

Salmon is super rich in omega 3 fatty acids. I know I have gone on and on about these vital fats in this book, but they are so important for both the long- and short-term health of your skin. For starters they help to keep the skin cell membranes supple and healthy, allowing them to take in nutrients more effectively and to clear waste more rapidly, thus helping to keep the whole organ healthy. Omega 3s are also vital for managing many skin conditions, such as eczema and acne, due to their inherent anti-inflammatory properties.

Sesame Soy Tuna Steaks with Sweet Potato Wedges

Serves 1

This is a great recipe for those days when you feel like you could eat a horse and chase the jockey! It is seriously filling, but won't overload with calories, and contains so much skin-friendly nutrition that I swear you can notice the difference the next morning!

2 tablespoons soy sauce
1 tablespoon sesame oil
1 teaspoon honey
1 fresh tuna steak
1 large sweet potato
1 clove of garlic

1. The first stage of this dish is to create the marinade, and marinate the tuna steak. Create the marinade by combining the soy sauce, sesame oil and honey together in a small bowl. Ensure that all three ingredients are well mixed into a glossy emulsion.
2. Add the tuna steak to the bowl, and roll it over and over in order to coat thoroughly in the marinade.
3. Marinate the steak for one hour, 30 minutes on each side.
4. Once the steak has been marinating for an hour, it's time to start cooking. Preheat the oven to 220°C/425°F/Gas Mark 7. Cut the sweet potato into wedges (leaving the skin on), and place in a roasting tin. Drizzle a little olive oil over the wedges, stir well, then place in the hot oven and roast for 20-25 minutes, stirring occasionally.

5. When the wedges have been roasting for about 15 minutes, heat a little olive oil in a shallow frying pan, and add the tuna steak. Fry for about 10 minutes, 5 minutes on each side.
6. Just before serving, finely chop the clove of garlic, and stir through the wedges. Return the wedges to the oven for another minute, then it's ready to serve.
7. Serve with a side salad.

Benefits

Tuna

Fresh tuna is another rich source of that ever wonderful nutrient, omega 3. See page 90 for full details of its virtues. Tuna is also rich in the minerals zinc and selenium. Zinc is vitally important for the regulation of sebaceous gland activity. If the skin is too oily, zinc can tone things down a little. Conversely, if the skin is too dry, zinc can stimulate the sebaceous glands to release extra sebum, helping skin composition. Selenium is the precursor to the body's formation of its own naturally occurring enzyme, called glutathione peroxidase. This powerful enzyme can help to minimize free radical levels in all tissues.

Sweet Potatoes

Sweet potatoes are packed up to the eyeballs with the potent fat-soluble antioxidant, beta carotene. It is what is responsible for that luscious deep orange flesh. If you recall from the antioxidants chapter, we need to maximize our intake of the fat-soluble varieties so that they can deliver their activity within our skin.

Thai Prawn (Shrimp) Curry

Serves 2-4

I love a good curry, and I am very fond of prawns (shrimps), so this is a winner for me. It's a slight diversion from a true Thai taste because it includes tomatoes, but with the red curry paste and the coconut, it gives a wonderful fusion flavour that is halfway between Indian and Thai. Good stuff!

1 red onion, finely chopped
1 clove of garlic, finely chopped
1 teaspoon freshly grated ginger
coconut oil
2 tablespoons Thai red curry paste
400 g/14 oz can of chopped tomatoes
1 x 50 g/2 oz sachet of coconut cream
400 g/14 oz prawns (shrimps) (fresh or frozen)

1. Sauté the onion, garlic and ginger in a little coconut oil, until the onion softens.
2. Stir in the red curry paste and sauté for a further 2 minutes, until fragrant.
3. Add in the tomatoes, and the coconut cream, and simmer for about 8 minutes, which will thicken the sauce considerably.
4. Add in the prawns (shrimps). If they were cooked, simmer for 3 minutes. If they were raw, simmer for about 8 minutes.
5. At the last minute I sometimes stir in a bit of spinach to add a dash of colour and extra nutrients.
6. Serve with quinoa and salad.

Benefits

Prawns (shrimps)
These are very dense in the minerals zinc and selenium. Selenium is one of the most commonly deficient trace elements in the Western world and is vitally important for the long-term health and protection of all tissues, including the skin. This is because it is the chemical precursor to the body's own inbuilt antioxidant enzyme, super oxide dismutase (SOD). This is a very powerful antioxidant that can protect all tissues, including the skin, from free radical damage. Zinc plays several vital roles in skin health. Firstly, it regulates the activity of the sebaceous glands, helping to normalize their secretions. Secondly, zinc is vital for regulating the activity of white blood cells, due to its role in controlling genetic activity within these cells. This makes zinc extra important in issues such as acne.

Tomatoes
Tomatoes are rich with another of the fat-soluble antioxidants lycopene. This antioxidant has long been promoted for male health, but is in fact fabulous for the long-term health of the skin. As a fat-soluble compound, it will naturally migrate into the fatty subcutaneous layer of the skin, where it can offer protection against free radical damage.

Red Onion
Red onions are one of my favourite ingredients. When it comes to skin health they have some great things to offer. They are a very rich source of dietary sulphur. This often forgotten mineral is a vital component in the manufacture of all connective tissues, including the extracellular matrix. This is the criss-cross lattice that is woven between tissues and collagen fibres which helps to give tissues their rigid structure. The skin is very dense in this structure, and we need to ensure we have a regular supply of dietary sulphur to maintain it. Red onions are also very rich in a group of powerful antioxidant compounds called flavonoids. These are the compounds that give them their deep purple colour pigment.

Spinach and Cannellini Bean Crumble

Serves 2-4

This beautiful filling dish provides real comfort food in the winter. Its plain title gives no hint of the magical flavour that is created when these ingredients are combined together.

2 cloves of garlic, finely chopped
1 x 400 g/14 oz can of cooked cannellini beans
3 large handfuls of baby spinach
5 slices of wholemeal bread
1 tablespoon butter

1. In a pan, add the chopped garlic to some very hot oil. This is one of those rare occasions where you want the garlic to actually begin to brown. This gives a nice aromatic, toasty flavour.
2. Half drain the cannellini beans, and add them with the remaining liquid to the garlic, along with a pinch of salt. Allow to simmer for a minute, before adding the baby spinach.
3. Add the bread to a food processor and process to make breadcrumbs.
4. Add the butter to a pan and melt. Once melted, add the breadcrumbs to the butter and mix thoroughly.
5. Preheat the oven to 200°C/400°F/Gas Mark 6. Place the cannellini bean mixture into a baking dish, and top with the buttered breadcrumbs. Bake in the oven until the topping has turned golden brown.

Benefits

Cannellini Beans

One of the frequently neglected parts of the skin health picture is good digestion and proper elimination of waste products. If we are not eliminating properly (and believe me, that's quite an epidemic these days), then we are not keeping the other routes of elimination clear. We start to create a rather nasty environment within our digestive tract. Waste products that don't leave the gut quickly enough can start to be absorbed back through the gut wall into circulation. This can lead to the other organs of elimination, such as the liver and the kidneys, being put under more pressure. Now, if these organs get overwhelmed at any time, the body will simply divert waste products to the skin for removal, as the skin is a very rapid and efficient route of elimination. The elimination of waste products through the skin has been linked with all manner of skin ailments, from acne to eczema. Cannellini beans, like all pulses, are very high in fibre, which helps to give additional bulk to the stool, and allows for a more rapid, easy and full elimination.

Spinach

Spinach is a wonderful source of beta carotene, one of the most potent fat-soluble antioxidants, that will penetrate the base layer of the skin and hang around there to offer protection against free radical damage.

Pasta with Spinach and Feta in Roasted Red (Bell) Pepper Sauce

Serves 2-4

I really like feta. I just can't get enough of the stuff. This is a great dish that screams Mediterranean sunshine, and loves your skin from within!

4 red (bell) peppers
**3 handfuls/150 g/6 oz approx wholewheat pasta (penne works
  well here)**
1 clove of garlic, finely chopped
1 red onion, finely chopped
2 handfuls of baby spinach
125 g/4½ oz feta cheese

1. Preheat the oven to 200°C/400°F/Gas Mark 6. Slice the (bell) peppers in half, remove and discard the seeds, and place sliced hollow side down into a baking tray, filled about 3mm deep with water. Place into the hot oven, and roast for about 20 minutes, until the (bell) pepper has softened and the skin has started to blacken.
2. While the (bell) peppers are roasting, start the pasta boiling in a large pan of water.
3. In a separate pan sauté the garlic and the onion until the onion has softened.
4. Remove the (bell) peppers from the oven and place into a food processor. Add the garlic and onion to the food processor along with a tablespoon of olive oil and a pinch of salt. Blend into a smooth sauce, and keep aside.

5. Once the pasta is cooked, drain it and place it into the pan that the onions and garlic were sautéed in. Add the sauce to the pasta and mix well. Return to the heat and add the spinach to the pasta and sauce mix. Keep stirring over the heat until the spinach has wilted.

6. Remove from the heat and serve with a side salad. Crumble over the feta cheese just before serving.

Benefits

Red (Bell) Peppers

Red (bell) peppers are very dense in beta carotene and alpha carotene, two potent members of the carotenoid family of fat-soluble antioxidants. These are the ones that migrate into the subcutaneous tissue and support the collagen fibres therein. Red (bell) peppers are also rich in a group of compounds called flavonoids. These show promise as skin protecting compounds that deliver both antioxidant and anti-inflammatory activity.

Spinach

Spinach is a rich source of fat-soluble antioxidant, beta carotene.

Red Onions

Red onions, like all the allium family, are very rich sources of dietary sulphur. This mineral is vital for the production and maintenance of the extracellular matrix. This is the network of dense fibres that attach to both soft tissues, and collagen and elastin fibres, to create a great deal of structural rigidity within a given tissue. The skin in particular is very dense in extracellular matrix. This rigid structure requires a constant supply of sulphur to maintain itself.

Note: The fat content of the feta and the olive oil will aid the body in the absorption of the fat-soluble compounds, which means that you will take up more of them than if you just ate those ingredients in isolation.

Balsamic Roasted Mediterranean Vegetables with White Bean and Rosemary Mash

Serves 2–4

This is heaven on a plate. I just love the Mediterranean influence in my diet, not only for the health benefits, but for the simple freshness of the flavours.

½ red (bell) pepper, sliced lengthways
½ courgette, sliced lengthways
1 red onion, halved and sliced lengthways
1 tablespoon balsamic vinegar
1 x 400 g/14 oz can of cannellini beans, drained
sprig of fresh rosemary, finely chopped
1 clove of garlic, finely chopped

1. Preheat the oven to 200°C/400°F/Gas Mark 6. Add the sliced vegetables to a roasting tin, and drizzle a little olive oil, plus the balsamic vinegar over them. Add a pinch of salt and mix well. Place in the hot oven and roast for about 25 minutes, stirring regularly.
2. Add the drained beans to a bowl, and mash with the back of a fork. Add a little olive oil to help you make a creamy texture. Add a pinch of salt, and the chopped rosemary, and mix well to form a creamy mash.
3. Once the vegetables are almost cooked, sprinkle the chopped garlic over them and return to the oven for 2 minutes.
4. Remove and serve the vegetables over the mash.

Benefits

Cannellini Beans

These gorgeous beans are a very rich source of the all-important B vitamins. These commonly deficient nutrients are involved in regulating so many processes within the skin. They help to regulate microcirculation to the upper middle layers of the skin, which evens out skin tone considerably. They help to regulate the turnover of skin cells, plus they are vital components in the correct metabolism of essential fatty acids into their metabolic end products that deliver so many benefits.

Red (Bell) Pepper

Red (bell) peppers are rich in the fat-soluble antioxidant, beta carotene. They are also very rich in a group of compounds called flavonoids. These are the chemicals responsible for the deep red colour. Flavonoids are by their very nature wonderful anti-inflammatories, so can be of great use in conditions such as acne and eczema. Both of these conditions feature characteristic lesions that involve a great deal of redness. This redness is a sign that there is active inflammation. With these conditions it is therefore worthwhile to consume as many naturally anti-inflammatory compounds as possible to support healing.

Red Onions

Like red (bell) peppers, red onions are very rich in flavonoids which are responsible for that rich red/purple colour. Onions, like all of the alliums, are also very rich in organic sulphur which helps to support the manufacture and maintenance of the extracellular matrix.

Beetroot (Beet), Red Onion and Goat's Cheese Tart

Serves 2

I just adore this dish. It is heavenly, and usually when I cook it I find myself having to make much more of the filling than I need to actually make the tart, as I find myself munching it as I go along.

1 large red onion
1 tablespoon honey
1 large sheet of puff pastry
4 large cooked beetroot (beet)
150 g/5 oz goat's cheese or feta

1. Add a small amount of olive oil to a large saucepan. Cut the red onion into thin slices, add to the oil and sauté until they begin to soften. At this point, add the honey, and continue to cook until the onion takes on a caramelized texture.
2. Roll out the ready-made puff pastry, to a size that is large enough to fit a 25 cm/10 inch round tart tin. Once rolled out, line the tin with pastry, and trim as necessary.
3. Preheat the oven to 200°C/400°F/Gas Mark 6. Begin by blind baking the pastry, covering the pastry with grease proof paper and filling with ceramic baking beads, or even some dried beans.
4. Once the pastry has been blind baked for about 10 minutes, remove the baking beads and paper to reveal the pastry case. Add the caramelized onions first, ensuring the whole base of the pastry case has been covered. Then dice the cooked beetroot (beet), and sprinkle over the top of the onion layer. Lastly, break the cheese up into little pieces all over the beetroot (beet) and onion mixture.

5. Return to the oven for around 10 minutes, or until the pastry is golden brown and the cheese is softening and beginning to get a few brown edges.

6. Serve with a side salad.

Benefits

Beetroot (Beet)

This is a very powerful food for liver health. Its deep purple pigment, that stains anything and everything, is given to the plant by a chemical called beta cyanin. Beta cyanin is known to be a stimulant of the phase 2 detoxification pathways in the liver. This helps to speed up and improve the way the liver deals with waste materials. The better the liver is functioning, the better the skin looks. This is because when the liver is overburdened, the skin is often used as a rapid route of elimination, which is believed by many to aggravate certain skin conditions such as eczema.

Red Onions

As has been mentioned before, the whole allium family is rich in sulphur to support extracellular matrix structure and function. Onions are also a very rich source of a prebiotic compound called inulin. This special type of sugar can be used as a food source by the good bacteria in the gut, to enhance their growth. Healthy gut flora is vital for good digestive function. If our digestive tract is healthy and we are breaking down food properly, and properly eliminating, this will be reflected in our skin.

11

Desserts

Raw Key Lime Pie

Serves 2-4

This is so delicious that you will struggle to believe that it is good for so many aspects of your health, and especially for your skin. I have given this dish to even the most hardcore junk food warriors, and they have loved it, not believing it was healthy. It is a beautiful, refreshing, zesty treat.

125 g/4½ oz uncooked walnuts
4 tablespoons flax seeds
5 pitted and chopped dates
2 tablespoons coconut oil
3 large ripe avocados
3 teaspoons honey
2 fresh limes

To Make the Base/Pie Crust
1. Place the nuts, flax seeds and dates into a food processor.
2. Gently melt 1 tablespoon of the coconut oil in a pan on a very low temperature. Pour the melted oil into the food processor, along with the nuts, etc, and process to form a dough.
3. Place the dough into a pie dish, and press down evenly to form a pie crust. Place in the fridge for 2-3 hours, until set.

To Make the Filling

1. Scoop the flesh out of the avocados into a food processor. Add in the honey, and the juice of the limes, along with the zest of one of the limes.
2. Melt the remaining 1 tablespoon of coconut oil in a small pan, and add the melted coconut oil to the food processor along with the avocados, etc, and blend into a smooth purée.
3. Remove the pie crust from the fridge, and transfer the avocado mixture into it. Return to the fridge to set. After an hour or so, the dish is ready to serve.

Benefits

Avocado

Avocados have wrongly been labelled an unhealthy food by some of these weird and wacky diet websites. Avocados are, in fact, a wonderfully healthy food, especially for the skin. They are a very rich source of the most famous fat-soluble antioxidant of them all – vitamin E!

Vitamin E, due to its fat-soluble nature, will move into the subcutaneous layer of the skin and protect all of the structural fibres from damage as the carotenoids, etc, do. The unique thing about vitamin E, though, is that it can act directly upon skin cells. It can help to protect the fatty outer lining of skin cells from being damaged by free radicals. This protection offers some help in slowing the ageing process, provided that we have a regular intake of this nutrient throughout our lives (let's remember how rapid the turnover of skin cells is).

Avocados are very dense in a group of fats called phytosterols, which deliver huge health benefits to the cardiovascular system, but are also known to have a significant anti-inflammatory activity.

As well as the above, avocados are rich in substances called polyhydroxylated fatty alcohols, which are known to assist in the absorption of fatty substances, including fat-soluble antioxidants!

Walnuts

Walnuts are another food that has started to make the headlines in recent months. Hysteria around nuts being a supposedly 'fattening' food has led to more focus on their actual benefits, and walnuts have certainly come up trumps. They are an extremely dense source of omega 3 fatty acids that we desperately need, especially to keep skin in tip-top condition. Walnuts are also a very rich source of zinc, which helps to regulate sebaceous secretions, helps to support the immune system and aids in wound healing.

Blueberry and Yogurt Layer Crunch

Serves 1

This is a very light and virtuous dessert, and is really great on a hot day, as it is very cooling with the yogurt and berries together.

Blueberries
Plain probiotic yogurt
Raw porridge oats
Golden flax seeds

You will notice that I haven't put specific weights, etc, for these ingredients. It's literally a case of having the ingredients handy, and creating the recipe in layers according to the size of your serving vessels.

1. Start with a layer of blueberries.
2. On top of that place a layer of yogurt, then a layer of oats, then a layer of flax seeds.
3. Repeat this process over and over until your serving vessel is full.

Benefits

Blueberries
Blueberries are packed with a very broad range of antioxidant compounds, some are water-soluble, and others, like the flavonoids, are fat-soluble and can make their way to the subcutaneous tissue. They are also a very rich source of vitamin C which is a vital component in the manufacture of collagen.

Flax Seeds
These luscious crunchy seeds are full of omega 3 fatty acids, which I'm sure by now you are 100 per cent familiar with. Inflammation-busting, skin-softening and all-round health-improvers!

Oats
Oats are great sources of the B vitamins. Remember, these often-deficient nutrients are involved, at one stage or another, in regulating almost every physiological response in the skin, whether it is circulation, or skin cell turnover, or even wound healing and oil secretion. Any food source that offers good levels of these nutrients will help the skin to function better as a whole organ.

Blackberry Crumble

Serves 2-4

This is one of my absolute favourites. I have to admit, I don't have much of a sweet tooth, so very often don't eat desserts at all, but if I'm feeling indulgent, this is a perfect example of what I'd reach for.

1 punnet of fresh blackberries (even better if you can go and pick them)
1 teaspoon honey
5 tablespoons porridge oats
½ teaspoon cinnamon

1. Preheat the oven to 200°C/400°F/Gas Mark 6. Place the berries, honey and a tablespoon of water into a pan and simmer over a high heat. The berries will begin to break down into a mush. Keep simmering the mix until it starts to thicken and resemble jam.
2. Once it has reached this texture, transfer the mix into a small ovenproof dish. Top the mixture with the oats and the cinnamon, and bake in the hot oven for 15-20 minutes, until the oats are a golden brown.

Benefits

Blackberries

Blackberries, like all of the dark berries, are very rich in a whole spectrum of antioxidants, including several fat-soluble compounds that make up part of the colour pigment found in this berry. These compounds will soon start to accumulate in the subcutaneous layer of the skin.

Oats

As well as keeping the digestive system ticking along nicely thanks to their fibre content, oats are also a very rich source of the B vitamins, which help to regulate almost every response needed to keep the skin functioning at its peak, thus making this massive organ function as well as it can.

12
Breakfasts

Brazil Nut, Walnut and Pumpkin Seed Muesli

Serves 1

This lovely recipe contains a broad spectrum of skin-loving nutrients so you will get your skin-nourishing-day off to a flying start.

Per Bowl
4 tablespoons porridge oats
1 tablespoon chopped walnuts
1 tablespoon chopped Brazil nuts
1 tablespoon pumpkin seeds

Nice and easy. Combine all the ingredients into a bowl and serve with rice milk or natural live yogurt. You could even scatter a few blueberries over to bump up the nutrient levels... not that it needs it!

Benefits

Oats

Oats are packed with B vitamins, the nutritional regulators of every conceivable aspect of skin health. They are especially rich in biotin which maintains the health of skin cells but also plays a vital role in the body's ability to correctly utilize fatty acids.

Walnuts

Walnuts are true superstars. New research on these wonderful nuts has show that their high oil content is a massive 94 per cent omega 3 fatty acids! This makes them one of the richest sources of these vital fats on the planet. Walnuts are also very high in the trace mineral zinc. Anyone with acne or eczema that has a tendency to become infected should definitely increase their zinc intake as its supportive effect upon immune function can certainly reduce the severity of such conditions.

Brazil Nuts

Brazils are another nutritional powerhouse. They are one of the richest sources of selenium on the planet. Selenium is the co factor for the production of glutathione peroxidase – a powerful antioxidant enzyme that is produced naturally within the body. While offering antioxidant protection to all tissues, glutathione peroxidase can also play a role in managing inflammation. This means that any skin conditions that involve areas of redness during flare-ups can be notably reduced by increasing selenium intake.

Pumpkin Seeds

Pumpkin seeds are another very rich source of zinc, so offer nutritional support to the immune system, useful for fighting acne and other infected skin lesions. They are also reasonably high in essential fatty acids. But, there are equal amounts of omega 6 and omega 3 in pumpkin seeds, so don't go too crazy with how many you consume as it is vital that we maintain that all-important ratio of twice the amount of omega 3 to omega 6 each day.

Smoked Salmon Eggs Benedict

Serves 1

This is my all-time favourite breakfast! I eat it at least 4 or 5 times a week. It is seriously nutrient-dense, tastes amazing, and is really rather a decadent affair too!

2 eggs
hollandaise sauce (OK, I admit it, I tend to buy a fresh readymade one, but feel free to make your own if you want)
½ wholemeal English muffin
2–3 slices of smoked salmon

1. Crack both eggs gently into a pan of boiling water, and poach for 3–4 minutes.
2. Warm the hollandaise sauce in a small pan.
3. Toast the half muffin. Place the smoked salmon slices onto the toasted muffin.
4. Place the poached eggs on top of the salmon slices.
5. Top the whole lot with enough hollandaise sauce to cover it well.

Benefits

Eggs

Eggs have got a bad rap over the years, but unjustly so. They are nutritional powerhouses. They are a very rich source of the B vitamins, so can drastically improve skin's overall functioning, as they regulate almost all metabolic activity within the different layers of the skin. Provided that the eggs are of reasonable quality, they should also provide a fair amount of omega 3 fatty acids.

Salmon

Salmon, as I'm sure you are aware at this stage in the book, is a wonderful source of omega 3 fatty acids which are one of the skin's best friends. These vital fats will keep the skin in an almost ageless state as they maintain moisture levels and the fluidity of skin cells. Salmon is also a rich source of the trace mineral selenium. This nutrient is the precursor to the formation of a compound called glutathione peroxidase, which is able to protect almost every tissue from free radical damage.

Breakfast Smoothie

Serves 1

This is a quick and easy morning smoothie that you can just pour into a container and run out the door with. Convenience is always good.

2 handfuls of frozen mixed berries
200 ml/7 fl oz rice milk or almond milk
1 scoop of whey protein powder (vanilla works best here)
2 tablespoons flax seed oil

Place all the ingredients into a blender, and blend into a thick luscious smoothie.

Benefits

Berries
All berries will naturally be rich in different antioxidant compounds. Having a mixture of different types of berries here will provide a broader scope of antioxidants, as different colour pigments relate to different types of antioxidants. Many of these will come into the fat-soluble category, so will offer those protective benefits that have been widely discussed throughout this book.

Whey Protein Powder
The protein powder has been included here just to regulate the impact this smoothie has upon blood sugar levels. Fruit contains very fast releasing sugars, which can cause very rapid rises in blood sugar. Sharp rises in blood sugar can cause cross linking of collagen fibres, causing the skin to lose elasticity, and causing the skin to age prematurely, not to mention the other damage that blood sugar spikes can cause. By adding a scoop of protein powder, this changes the whole picture. It causes the sugars to be released at a very slow rate, which doesn't upset blood sugar levels in the slightest, and will have the added bonus of keeping you fuller for longer.

Flaxseed Oil
Flax oil is a very good source of omega 3 fatty acids. While it doesn't provide the full spectrum of these vital components in the same way as fish sources, it does come pretty close. So this should be another addition to your daily routine for moist, plump, smooth skin. It has a lovely light taste that can easily be disguised by flavours such as berries.

Spinach and Feta Breakfast Scramble

Serves 1

This is a gorgeous dish. Be warned though, it's only for those days when you are very hungry as it is one of those dishes that will fill you up until lunch time.

2 handfuls of baby spinach leaves
3 eggs
80 g/3 oz feta cheese, cubed

1. Add the baby spinach to a pan with a little olive oil and sauté until it wilts.
2. Crack the eggs into a bowl, and whisk them with a fork.
3. Add the eggs to the pan with the spinach on a high heat, and stir continuously. As soon as the first signs of scrambled egg start to appear, throw in the cubed feta and continue stirring. Once all of the egg is scrambled, it is ready to serve.

Benefits

Eggs

Eggs are packed with B vitamins, to support daily skin function, and also a broad range of essential fatty acids.

Spinach

Spinach is packed with so many goodies, it is ridiculous. It is a very rich source of beta carotene, one of the most powerful compounds in the fat-soluble antioxidant category, so will migrate into the subcutis and offer its support there.

13
Drinks

A note about these recipes:

These recipes will generally require a juicer and/or a blender. If you have never tried making your own juices at home, then it really is worth having a go. It used to be a very laborious and messy affair, but now the modern juicers make it an absolute breeze, and are a doddle to clean. The beauty of juices is that you get a huge amount of nutrition in a very small and easy-to-consume delivery system. You get the nutrients found in several servings of fresh produce, without having to sit down and devour it all. It is also worth investing in a decent blender.

Skin Tonic Tea

OK, I couldn't resist it. As I am a medical herbalist, I thought it only right that I should use some of these wonderful tools in this book. Dried herbs are easy to obtain, and herbal teas are wonderful to sip on throughout the day. Don't underestimate the power of a tea though. Much of the active chemistry in medicinal plants will be water-soluble, and something as simple as creating an infusion will in fact create a powerful chemical cocktail. I usually brew my teas in a medium sized cafetière. All of these herbs are freely available at a reputable herbal supplier (see useful contacts section).

Per Pot
2 teaspoons dried red clover
2 teaspoons dandelion leaf
2 teaspoons cleavers
2 teaspoons calendula

Now, I hope you are paying attention here... simply add all the herbs to the pot, and cover with hot water! Steep for about 10–15 minutes before drinking.

Benefits

Red Clover
Red clover is one of my favourite skin herbs. It seems to have an amazing ability to reduce the movement of waste products through the skin. As has been explained earlier in this book, the skin can easily be used as a route of elimination for waste material. It is a norm for many of us to be bombarded by all manner of challenging compounds in our modern world, which put a certain amount of strain upon our organs of elimination such as the liver and kidneys. When these are already hard at work, the body will start to look at other ways to get rid of waste products. It is actually very easy for the body to send some of this gunk out through the skin for rapid removal. However, many people believe that this can be a trigger for some skin conditions to flare up or worsen.

Dandelion Leaf

Dandelion leaves are a very powerful natural diuretic. This means that they stimulate the kidneys to increase urinary output. This helps the kidneys to remove water-soluble waste components far quicker and reduces the likelihood that waste products are sent for removal via the skin.

Cleavers

Cleavers, otherwise known as goose grass or sticky willy, are a very powerful herb for keeping the lymphatic system clean. The lymphatic system is almost like a second circulatory system that basically drains all the gunk and rubbish that has been released from all cells in all tissues. Cells eject their waste products into lymphatic fluid, which bathes them. This fluid then makes its way to lymphatic vessels, on route to the kidneys for removal. The movement of lymphatic fluid around these vessels is dependent upon muscular contraction to physically squeeze the fluid along on its way. This can sometimes mean that it takes a while for waste products to get to the kidneys for removal. Cleavers contain a group of chemicals called coumarins (these are the same chemicals you smell when someone cuts the grass). These compounds cause the walls of the lymphatic vessels to contract. This contraction increases the pressure within the vessel. When the pressure increases it takes less effort to move more lymphatic fluid further which, in short, will lead to faster removal of waste products from the lymphatic fluid; again, keeping everything nice and clean and lessening the risk of waste products being routed through the skin for removal.

Calendula

Calendula has a long history of being a great herb for skin health. The bright orange colour pigments in the flower petals are very effective anti-inflammatory agents, and have been traditionally used during skin flare-ups for centuries. Calendula, like cleavers, is also a great lymphatic tonic, helping to keep this system clean.

Raspberry and Melon Cooler

Serves 1

This is such a delicious drink, and served in a cool glass on a hot day just brings visions of relaxing on a beach somewhere. Nice!

150 g/5 oz fresh raspberries
½ water melon
1 apple
sparkling mineral water

Run all the ingredients through a juicer. When serving, fill up a glass two-thirds, and then top up the remaining with the sparkling water.

Benefits

Raspberries
Raspberries are a wonderful source of vitamin C and, when consumed in their raw state like this, the vitamin C levels will remain intact. Vitamin C, as you will recall, is a vitally important factor for the production of collagen. So, if you want to keep skin young and healthy, a good consistent intake of vitamin C is essential.

Water Melon
Water melons are dense in several important nutrients. Like raspberries they are a rich source of vitamin C, for collagen support. They are also very high in beta carotene, that champion of fat-soluble antioxidants.

Green Smoothie

This recipe is an absolute winner! I have made this smoothie on numerous radio and TV shows, often to the disbelief of the presenters. They look at what goes into it, and the colour of it, and are shocked when they actually taste it and love every drop. You will be shocked. It contains loads of greens, but all you will taste is the fruit.

1 banana
1 handful of red grapes
2 large handfuls of baby spinach leaves
200 ml/7 fl oz apple juice

Add all the ingredients to a blender and blend into an iridescent green smoothie.

Benefits

Spinach
Huge amounts of beta carotene, plus vitamin C, and anti-inflammatory compounds such as the flavonoids. Spinach is also rich in minerals including nice levels of zinc, gram for gram.

Red Grapes
Red grapes are a rich source of collagen boosting vitamin C. They are host to a very broad spectrum of antioxidants, most commonly, the heart healthy anthocyanins. Their array of fat-soluble antioxidants also provides protection to the subcutaneous structural components.

Carrot, Apple, Beetroot (Beet) and Celery Juice

Serves 1

This deeply coloured juice is incredibly potent. I know it may seem weird to a lot of you to drink vegetable juices with fruit juices, but I assure you, it is very tasty. The sweetness of the apple really comes through and takes your mind off the fact that there are veggies in there.

1 large carrot
1 large apple
1 small raw beetroot (beet)
2 sticks of celery

Simply run all the ingredients through a juicer... and that's it!

Benefits

Carrots
Carrots are a very dense source of beta carotene. This is, of course, the plant form of vitamin A, and the most powerful of the carotenoids – the fat-soluble antioxidants. Just to give you an idea as to how well these compounds accumulate in the subcutaneous layer of the skin, there is a condition called hypercarotenemia. This is where the skin of people who eat a lot of carrots will actually turn orange due to the sheer level of carotenoids that have accumulated in the skin. That's proof!

Apples
Apples have a high vitamin C content, and also contain a powerful chemical called ellagic acid. This has well documented antioxidant properties and is believed by some to be an effective liver stimulant, helping in the detoxification process. The jury is still out on that one though.

Beetroot (Beet)
Beetroot (beet), on the other hand, does have a very powerful effect upon liver function. The deep purple colour pigment so characteristic of it influences phase 2 detoxification in the liver, which can help to keep things on the inside clean. It also contains a huge amount of fat-soluble antioxidants.

Celery
Celery is a very rich source of so many minerals, including potassium, sodium and magnesium. These minerals help to keep the body hydrated. There is nothing worse for the overall appearance of the skin than dehydration. The minerals in celery make it a very hydrating juice. However, there is a dichotomy here. Celery also has a mild diuretic effect, meaning it increases urinary output. It has the ability to make the kidneys work a little harder, without overdoing it to the point where someone would get dehydrated.

Spinach, Cucumber and Cantaloupe Melon Juice

Serves 1

This is an amazing tasting juice. Sweet, fragrant, divine. Not to mention the nutrient density.

2 handfuls of baby spinach leaves
½ cucumber
¼ cantaloupe melon

Run all the ingredients through a juicer. Put the spinach leaves in first and use the other ingredients to push them through.

Benefits

Cucumber

Cucumbers are surprisingly nutrient dense. They provide vitamin C and some minerals. The most interesting mineral is silica. This is the mineral responsible for the luscious shiny skin of the cucumber. Silica is a vital component in the manufacture of collagen and also the maintenance of its flexibility, helping the skin to become more resilient to sagging and wrinkling.

Cantaloupe Melon

This is included in this juice for two main reasons. Firstly, its flavour absolutely complements that of cucumber beautifully. Secondly and most importantly, it is a very rich source of carotenoids, those by now familiar fat-soluble antioxidants. There is also a reasonable amount of vitamin C in cantaloupes too.

Spinach

Spinach is another rich source of vitamin C surprisingly! Gram for gram it has more vitamin C than an orange. There is, of course, also a huge dose of beta carotene in spinach leaves, making this juice a fat-soluble antioxidant bath for your skin.

Useful Contacts

Here are some useful companies and services. Please note that I was not paid to put these listings in here. These are companies that I genuinely feel offer useful products or services for those on a quest for better skin health, and ones that I know through personal usage.

The British Skin Foundation
www.britishskinfoundation.org.uk
A useful informational resource and charity for skin disorders.

Green People
www.greenpeople.co.uk
Green People offer a very wide range of skin care and body care products that are not only environmentally sound but are also very clean, and free of many of the nasty chemicals that dominate the commercial high street type skin products.

Neal's Yard Remedies
www.nealsyardremedies.com
Neal's Yard Remedies have a vast range of natural and very clean skincare products made to a very high standard. They also sell loose herbs, so are the ideal stockist for the ingredients to my herbal tea recipe on page 175.

Viridian Nutrition
www.viridian-nutrition.com
Viridian Nutrition offer a wide range of nutritional supplements that are made using ethically sourced ingredients, and that don't contain any artificial additives. My reason for recommending them here though is their range of nutritional oils, which provide essential fatty acids so widely discussed in this book.

Index